# THE *gourmet* NUTRITIONAL THERAPY COOKBOOK

BY LINDA LAZARIDES

WATERFALL 2000

LONDON

**Other books by Linda Lazarides**

Principles of Nutritional Therapy
The Nutritional Health Bible
The Waterfall Diet
The HIV Self-Help Manual

© 2000 Linda Lazarides
First published in 2000 by
Waterfall 2000
BCM Waterfall
London WC1N 3XX
United Kingdom

Linda Lazarides asserts the moral right to be identified as the author of this work.

ISBN  0-9538046-1-5

Printed and bound in Great Britain by Olivers Printers, Bexhill-on-Sea

# CONTENTS

This book is not intended as medical advice.
Consult your doctor before using it to treat any health problems,
especially if you have been placed on a medical diet.

## ACKNOWLEDGEMENTS

I would like to thank all those who have helped to produce this book, especially Carolyn Gibbs, for her excellent recipes and research into tracking down sources of blueberries! Also everybody at Olivers Printers for the printing and production, and Doug Young for typesetting the cover.

A special word of thanks goes to Lauren Anderson, without whose healing treatments and advice I don't think this book would have been possible, and Elizabeth Oliver and Adele Lewis for their help in guiding me along the road to better health.

Clipart by
GSP (Global Software Publishing) Ltd, Huntingdon, UK
and Microsoft Corporation (Publisher2000)

# FOREWORD

As a sufferer of M.E. (severe chronic fatigue syndrome), I had always felt that somewhere out there was a diet that would help me on the road to recovery. When I discovered nutritional therapy I knew that at last I had found the right one.

I'm a great believer in "you are what you eat," and through the practice of nutritional therapy I began to appreciate just how true this maxim is. For me it was to mean the difference between a bed-ridden existence and being able to get out of bed in the mornings. It was to mean the difference between despair and the realization that life did, after all, have so much more to offer.

Through Linda Lazarides I have learned that food is not just fuel for hungry tummies. As in my own case, therapeutic diets are tailor-made to tackle serious health problems, and specific foods are used to enhance well-being and the general state of health.

But this does not have to mean a life sentence of bland and boring meals. People often ask me, "But what do you *eat*?" My answer is simple—a great variety of foods! Through nutritional therapy I have been introduced to a whole wealth of ingredients that I would not previously have thought of using. Having to leave behind fast-foods, wheat, dairy produce and sugar has really been no hardship at all. On the contrary, not only have I benefited health-wise, which alone was enough to encourage me to change my eating habits, but also, with inspirational and creative recipes such as those featured in this cookbook, I never feel deprived.

But can recipes as delicious-sounding as these *really* be therapeutic? Well, my taste-buds might not quite believe it each time I savour Blueberry and Apple Crispy Pancakes, or Frittata with Ginger and Courgettes, served with Corfu-Style Garlic Potatoes, but my body certainly does!

*Carolyn Gibbs*

# What is Nutritional Therapy?

Many people find nutritional therapy a highly effective treatment for a number of distressing health problems, including:

- Irritable bowel syndrome
- Migraine
- Skin ailments
- High cholesterol/blood pressure
- Fluid retention
- Enlarged prostate
- Indigestion
- Period pains—especially in teenagers and young women
- Premenstrual syndrome
- Chronic fatigue

It is also the oldest medicine in the world: the medicine given to sailors who contracted a mysterious disease that could be fatal on long sea voyages—now known as scurvy and caused by a lack of vitamin C.

The medicine given to cure the mentally ill people who filled the psychiatric hospitals in 1930s America and who are now known to have suffered from a B vitamin deficiency called pellagra.

Many of us have already been prescribed nutritional therapy, for instance to treat:

- Anaemia
- Osteoporosis (brittle bone disease)
- Coeliac disease (a chronic diarrhoea and wasting condition), or
- To prevent spina bifida, (the incomplete development of a newborn baby's brain and spinal cord).

More controversially, you may have heard of nutritional therapy as an alternative therapy for diseases such as cancer.

If you feel under the weather, or have niggling ailments or perhaps more serious health problems, and if you are wondering whether nutritional therapy might also be able to help you or a loved one, here are some important facts:

Nutritional therapy works by treating:

- Nutritional deficiencies (these are *far* more common than you think),
- Food intolerances (abnormal reactions to normal foods),
- Dietary imbalances (e.g. too much alcohol, coffee, fat, salt or sugar),
- An overloaded liver due to pollution or to dysbiosis—too many toxin-producing bacteria in the intestines.

## HOW DOES THIS APPROACH HELP ILLNESS?

How well you feel depends on how efficiently your body produces essential enzymes, hormones and other substances, and gets rid of wastes and toxins that could interfere with your internal chemistry. Nutritional deficiencies can obviously make things go wrong. You may realize this and perhaps you have already taken steps to improve your diet. However deficiencies are not just caused by a faulty diet but also by:

- A lack of sufficient digestive juices to break down your food,
- Inflamed intestines (often due to toxin-producing bacteria) which have trouble getting nutrients from your food into your blood, where they are needed,
- Problems experienced by cells which need nutrients, in extracting those nutrients from your blood.

The recipes and information given in this book can help you with these problems and so improve your body's efficiency and fighting forces.

## HOW DO I KNOW IF IT WILL HELP ME?

While persistent health problems should always be reported to a doctor, nutritional therapy can often be used together with orthodox medicine. The Questionnaire on page 9 is to help you pinpoint how much benefit you could gain from following the eating guidelines and recipes in this book.

If several symptoms apply to you, your body's efficiency is being compromised by some of the problems listed on this page.

The recipes and advice in this book target these problems, to help you make the hormones and enzymes you need and to reduce inflammation and unwanted wastes. Here are just some of the benefits you could gain within just a few months:

- Generally feeling better and sleeping better.
- More energy.
- Better skin.
- Fewer headaches.
- Better digestion.
- You may be able to avoid a gall bladder operation or hysterectomy.
- You could in time be weaned off any unpleasant medications you are taking.
- Find out if your doctor could be wrong that you need to take drugs for the rest of your life for your blood pressure, arthritis, colitis, asthma, psoriasis etc.

It all makes such good sense, why wait any longer? After all, you have nothing to lose, so get cooking!

## HOW TO USE THE QUESTIONNAIRE

Only tick the boxes in the Questionnaire opposite if the symptom is persistent or quite noticeable. Count up the number of boxes you have ticked in each section and put the scores below.

| | |
|---|---|
| 1. Nutritional Deficiency and Dietary Imbalance score | |
| 2. Food Intolerance score | |
| 3. Overloaded Liver score | |

### IF YOUR SCORE FOR 1 IS HIGHER THAN THREE

You probably have some nutritional deficiencies. The higher your score, the more deficiencies you have and the more you need to follow the principles in this book. Remember, it is not just the deficiency symptoms you are treating, but the ailments that the deficiencies are encouraging.

### IF YOUR SCORE FOR 2 IS TWO OR MORE

It is quite likely that certain foods are not agreeing with you and are causing some of your symptoms. Carry out the Food Intolerance Test on pages 156-157 to find out which foods are responsible.  A score of 4 or more means you could also benefit from the Intestinal Healing Programme on page 160.

### IF YOUR SCORE FOR 3 IS TWO OR MORE

The Detoxification Soup on page 39 is especially for you, and should be eaten frequently. Follow the Liver Rejuvenation programme given on page 158. The Intestinal Healing Programme on page 160 could also help you.

# NUTRITIONAL THERAPY QUESTIONNAIRE

## Symptoms of Nutritional Deficiency and Dietary Imbalance

### Eyes
- ❏ Abnormally poor vision in bad light
- ❏ Dry eyes
- ❏ Sensitivity to bright lights

### Skin and Fingernails
- ❏ Spotty skin (acne)
- ❏ Dry, flaky skin
- ❏ Dandruff
- ❏ Puffy skin & fluid retention
- ❏ Itchy red patches
- ❏ Eczema
- ❏ Sore, raw tongue
- ❏ Sores that won't heal
- ❏ Split or brittle fingernails
- ❏ White-spotted fingernails

### Immune System
- ❏ Frequent colds or infections
- ❏ Persistent thrush

### Brain and Nervous System
- ❏ "Spaced-out" feeling
- ❏ Deteriorating co-ordination
- ❏ Increasing confusion
- ❏ Mood swings
- ❏ Poor concentration
- ❏ Tremors
- ❏ Easily startled

### Muscles
- ❏ Cramps
- ❏ Difficulty relaxing

### Hormones
- ❏ Premenstrual syndrome
- ❏ Painful periods
- ❏ Enlarged prostate
- ❏ Maturity-onset diabetes

### Bones
- ❏ Pain and tenderness
- ❏ Brittleness (osteoporosis)

### Miscellaneous
- ❏ Easy exhaustion
- ❏ Easy bruising
- ❏ Irregular heartbeats
- ❏ Palpitations
- ❏ Poor appetite
- ❏ Poor sense of taste or smell
- ❏ Many symptoms of internal pollution and liver stress

## Symptoms of Food Intolerance
- ❏ Chronic fatigue or unexplained daytime drowsiness
- ❏ Head feels "foggy"
- ❏ Sudden bouts of unusual aggression or depression
- ❏ Skin rashes
- ❏ Frequent severe headaches
- ❏ Diarrhoea or severe constipation or both (alternating)
- ❏ Griping tummy pains with or without mucus discharge
- ❏ Painful or swollen joints
- ❏ Frequently congested sinuses
- ❏ Fluid retention
- ❏ Chronic catarrh
- ❏ Wheezing and breathing difficulties
- ❏ Dark colour under your eyes
- ❏ Symptoms of poor digestion and absorption: frequently bloated, uncomfortable tummy with much gas. Sometimes undigested food in stools.

## Overloaded Liver
- ❏ Many nagging headaches
- ❏ Often slightly nauseous
- ❏ Head often feels "foggy"
- ❏ Skin problems
- ❏ Great lethargy
- ❏ Bad reactions to chemicals
- ❏ Yellowish skin or eyes
- ❏ Feeling unwell after coffee or small amount of alcohol
- ❏ Tenderness under right-hand ribs
- ❏ Many food intolerance symptoms

# THE HEALTHY PLATE

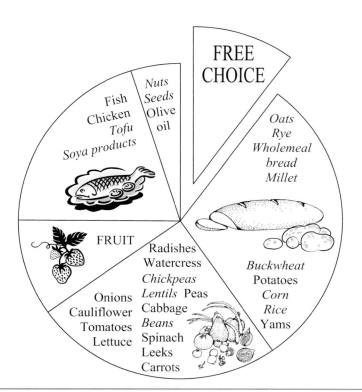

FREE CHOICE

Nuts
Seeds
Olive oil

Fish
Chicken
Tofu
Soya products

Oats
Rye
Wholemeal
bread
Millet

FRUIT

Radishes
Watercress
Chickpeas
Lentils Peas
Cabbage
Beans
Spinach
Leeks
Carrots

Onions
Cauliflower
Tomatoes
Lettuce

Buckwheat
Potatoes
Corn
Rice
Yams

Imagine the chart on the left is a picture of an ideal meal. The nearer you can get to this ideal, the better your body will be able to perform for you. After all, if you don't give a car the right fuel, it will break down eventually.

Your body has more anti-breakdown features than your car does, but it can't cope forever with a faulty diet!

Think of this chart as something to aim for. It is also a useful yardstick since a lot of published health advice can be quite confusing. Here you can clearly see the proportions you need. The *Free Choice* segment means that 10 per cent of your food can be anything else that is not on the chart.

- **Wheat flour, wheat pasta, wheat cereals and all foods containing wheat.**
- **Cow's milk and products made with it: butter, yoghurt, cheese and cream, casein (milk protein) and whey.**
- **Yeast, as found in yeast extract, spreads, stock cubes, gravy and sauce flavourings and mixes, alcoholic drinks and most types of bread and pizza.**
- **Hen's eggs in any form**
- **Artificial food additives**
- **Sugar, syrup and honey**
- **Red meat/animal fat***
- **Hydrogenated fat**
- **Salt* and sodium-based baking powder**

*There is one recipe for liver, and a few call for sheep's yoghurt or goat's cheese, which contain some animal fat. Several recipes call for miso or tamari sauce, which do contain some salt but are otherwise beneficial. Those on a salt-free diet should omit them.

# WHAT'S OMITTED FROM THE CHART AND THE RECIPES, AND WHY?

The panel on the left shows a list of the ingredients omitted from this book. You can see why people on nutritional therapy need a good recipe book. They often exclaim in horror "But what is there left to eat?" when their therapist asks them to avoid all these foods.

## WHEAT, DAIRY, EGGS AND YEAST

In order to be able to help as many people as possible, this book assumes that you may be one of the estimated 30 per cent of the population with a food intolerance. (The symptoms of food intolerance are listed on page 9.) If you do have a food intolerance, your problem food(s) will probably be one of these four. To find out whether it is safe for you to eat them and products made with them, test yourself following the instructions on pages 156-157.

Miso and tamari sauce are not fermented with commercial yeasts, and are usually safe for yeast-free diets.

## ARTIFICIAL FOOD ADDITIVES

Large numbers of people are known to be sensitive to these chemicals. For instance, sulphur-based preservatives may trigger asthma and digestive inflammation, and colourings can cause disturbed behaviour in some children. Certain colourings can react with bacteria in the intestines to form cancer-causing chemicals. Additives originally thought safe to eat have later been banned. The sweetener aspartame, used as tablets and in countless "diet" products such as yoghurt, cola and ice-cream and by diabetics is now causing worries since it has been linked with headaches, memory loss, eye problems and seizures.

One of the greatest concerns about additives is the unknown effect of mixing them together as we eat different foods containing them.

The remaining ingredients in the panel are covered in the next five pages.

# SUGAR, HONEY AND SYRUP

Sugar, a form of carbohydrate, is a natural component of fruit and vegetables, where it is not in concentrated form. Concentrated sugar is found in products such as honey, syrup and treacle, which are mainly sugar and water. The most concentrated form of sugar is the brown or white crystals we buy in packets, which are added to drinks or found in soda pops, ice cream, milk shakes, cakes, biscuits, cookies, jam, desserts, sweets and chocolate. In this form, the average person in the UK consumes about two pounds of sugar a week.

Most of us know that eating too much sugar is bad for our teeth and probably not good for our health. The big question is, how much is too much?

Let's look at it this way. We can only eat a certain number of calories a day without putting on excess weight. If one third of those calories come from sugar, you are eating only two thirds of the vitamin-rich food which a person on a low-sugar diet eats, since sugar consists of calories and no other nutrients. If you don't believe that one third or more of your diet consists of sugar, read on.

If you are consuming the national average of two pounds of sugar per week, that comes to about 150 grams a day. Each gram of sugar yields four Calories, making 600 Calories a day from sugar—or about one third of a normal calorie intake for a woman and one quarter of a normal calorie intake for a man.

Add to this the 30-40 per cent of our diet that comes from fat, and you can see how dangerously high your diet could be in "empty" calories—that is to say foods which provide only calories and virtually no other nutrients at all.

Of course, a national average sugar consumption of two pounds a week means that most people will be consuming either

## Did You Know?

When advertisements for sugar claim that sugar "gives you energy", they are not using the term "energy" in the usual sense of the word—i.e. helping you to *feel* more energetic. All our energy needs can be met by consuming a normal diet containing no added sugar at all. In fact, energy is a scientific term for calories, so the ads are really just telling you that sugar will provide you with calories!

more or less than this amount. If you know that you consume a lot of sugary foods and drinks, your total intake of empty calories could be as much as 80 per cent of your diet.

Your body is not going to react right away to being treated like this. It is very good at coping silently. But in time you could develop vitamin and mineral deficiency symptoms, such as

- Skin problems
- Lacking energy and stamina
- Frequent colds or thrush
- Period pains or PMS
- Diabetes
- Enlarged prostate.

If your liver does not get enough vitamins and minerals to make essential enzymes, it could start to have difficulty processing wastes and pollutants, which in turn can lead to inflammation in your skin or joints, fluid retention, headaches, lethargy and accelerated ageing. A weakening of your immune system reduces your body's ability to protect itself against cancer.

Taking vitamin pills to compensate for the empty calories is not the solution—hundreds of medical studies are showing that the people with the highest *fruit and vegetable* consumption are those least likely to get cancer and heart disease. These foods contain a lot of important nutrients besides vitamins and minerals.

Apart from depriving you of protective nutrients, consuming a lot of sugar makes you produce a lot of insulin, a hormone which allows you to absorb the sugar into your cells. Scientific trials show that high insulin levels encourage high fat levels in your blood, and cholesterol deposits on your artery walls. Your blood also becomes more "sticky", and so prone to tiny blood clots that could lead to a heart attack as you get older.

It really is worth cutting sugary foods and drinks down to 20 per cent or less of your calorie intake, along with most hard fats. Wouldn't you like to approach old age feeling fit and well rather than on a cocktail of medications for high cholesterol, high blood pressure and diabetes?

# FATS AND OILS

### ANIMAL FAT

Most of us know by now that animal fats such as butter and lard and the hidden fat in minced meat and burgers can encourage excess cholesterol in our blood. They are mainly saturated fats—also known as hard fats because they are solid at room temperature.

While animal fats tend to consist of little more than calories, some hard fats derived from plants do also contain useful ingredients, for instance

- Sterols, found in a variety of plant fats and oils, block the absorption of cholesterol from the diet,
- Tocotrienols, found in palm oil/fat, have cholesterol-lowering properties,
- Isoflavones, found in many plant fats and oils, are excellent balancers of the female hormone oestrogen and can also help to prevent prostate cancer,

- Lauric acid, found in coconut oil/fat, can inactivate many viruses and bacteria, including the "stealth" microbes which are now thought to be responsible for some types of severe chronic fatigue. Stealth microbes can evade detection by the immune system or by normal medical tests.

One of the dangers of consuming too much saturated fat is that the delicate outer membranes which cover our cells could become too rigid. This can especially affect the ability of oxygen-carrying red blood cells to squeeze through narrow blood vessels (capillaries) in your brain, eyes etc. Inflexible red cells can block your capillaries, leading to a poorer blood (and oxygen) supply to your brain, especially if you are an elderly person.

Most types of margarine are artificially hardened fats and rarely contain the above-mentioned beneficial ingredients.

## Olive Oil

Can be used in salads, dips, mayonnaises and for frying up to medium heat. Use the very beneficial "extra-virgin" variety, which is the very special first pressing of the olives, and is made without heating the oil, if the olive oil will form part of the dish. Use ordinary olive oil (which is cheaper) if it is only needed for frying.

## Groundnut Oil

Can also be used for frying, especially when the strong taste of olive oil is not wanted. Like olive oil, it is not rapidly damaged by heat.

## Polyunsaturated Oils

**Sunflower, safflower, soya oil, flax seed oil, hemp oil, walnut oil— use only cold, for salad dressings, mayonnaise, dips etc.**

## Coconut Oil

**Is hard at room temperature and so technically is a saturated fat. But studies have shown that it does not raise cholesterol like butter does. Use it for pastry– and cake-making. Coconut oil is also a traditional ingredient of many oriental dishes and curries. You can find it in shops that specialize in Asian cookery.**

### ESSENTIAL FATTY ACIDS

Another problem with animal fats is that they are usually poor in *essential fatty acids*, or EFAs. EFAs are similar to vitamins. They are substances derived from oily foods like nuts and seeds, which your body needs in relatively small amounts. These EFAs must be derived from your food— your body cannot manufacture them.

Essential fatty acids are especially needed by your cell membranes. They keep them supple and able to do their important job of aiding the entry of oxygen and nutrients into your cells and the exit of various waste products. So don't think that all fats are bad. The oily fats found in nuts and seeds are very beneficial indeed, although of course like any fatty or oily food you do have to watch out for the calorie content. Fortunately these naturally oily foods keep you feeling full for longer than carbohydrates, so they may help you to eat less.

As you will see from the recipes in this book, there are lots of interesting ways to incorporate nuts and seeds into your diet.

### HYDROGENATED FATS

You may find these listed as an ingredient on packets of biscuits, cookies, ice-cream etc. In some catering establishments, fish-and-chip shops and so on, foods are deep-fried in hydrogenated fats. Hydrogenated fats are usually oils which have been treated with hydrogen to make them hard at room temperature. Many brands of margarine and "vegetable fat" are made in this way. Sometimes they are only partially hydrogenated, which reduces the hardness to a "soft margarine" consistency. Some recent research has linked a high consumption of partially hydrogenated fats with a higher risk of heart disease.

### "TRANS" FATS

Commercial processing of oils and fats frequently creates an unnatural type of fat molecule known as the "trans" form. These trans fats can grab enzymes in your body which are needed before you can use your essential fatty acids. So consuming too much highly processed fat or oil can in time produce the effects of an EFA deficiency even if you are consuming enough EFAs.

# SALT

Foods high in salt (sodium chloride) include preserved meats (bacon, ham, salami, sausages, pork pies, etc.) smoked fish, canned fish, soy sauce, yeast extract, some cheeses, salted butter, salted peanuts and other packet snacks, most bread and stock cubes, and ready-made meals, soups and sauces. These foods, plus adding salt at the table can easily lead to a salt intake of 12-17 grams a day. The World Health Organisation recommends no more than 5 grams.

A high salt intake has been linked with

- Fluid retention
- High blood pressure and weight gain (as a result of fluid retention)
- Osteoporosis (brittle bone disease)
- A worsening of asthma.

In her book *A Matter of Life*, medical doctor and biochemist Dr Nadya Coates points out that when it comes into contact with water in our bodies, salt breaks down to hydrochloric acid and caustic soda—a highly irritating substance which can damage our cells and can occasionally cause odd burning sensations for which no medical cause can be found.

The best way to control salt is to eat food which you have prepared yourself, so you know exactly how much salt you have put in it. Low-sodium salt products are now available in supermarkets, and can help to cut your salt intake by 50 per cent or more. The recipes in this book will also help you to cut your salt intake drastically, but some use a little tamari sauce or miso, oriental flavourings which do contain salt but are also very rich in other nutrients. If you have been placed on a totally salt-free diet you could omit these or use potassium salt instead.

Baking powder contains bicarbonate of soda, which has effects similar to those of salt. See page 24 for suppliers of alternatives to sodium salt and baking powder.

# WHAT SHOULD I DRINK?

Scientists estimate that most of us need to drink at least five to six pints (3-4 litres) of liquid a day - more if you are breast-feeding, or if you suffer from heavy periods, diarrhoea or tend to sweat heavily. You should drink this amount even if you don't feel thirsty. Thirst only begins once dehydration has started. Signs of severe dehydration include dry skin, sunken eyes, mental confusion, constipation and concentrated urine. Chiropractors sometimes cure back pain and painful joints by treating dehydration—asking people to drink more water and less tea and coffee.

The best drink of all is plain water. Drink it on its own, or use it to dilute fruit juice. A mixture of sparkling water and fresh fruit juice is delicious, and much better for you than canned fizzy drinks, which are often high in sodium and sugar or artificial chemicals. Weak fruit or herb teas such as rosehip, blackcurrant, fennel or chamomile—preferably without sugar—are also good choices, and can be drunk hot or cold (with ice). Certain fruit or vegetable juices and herbal teas can help combat health problems, and this book includes some useful suggestions and recipes. Drinking a glass of cold water is an instant remedy any time your stomach feels unsettled.

The worst drinks for your health are tea, coffee and alcohol, because of their diuretic effect. A diuretic stimulates your body to excrete fluid more rapidly, even when its fluid levels are already low.

Alcohol can particularly dehydrate you as it reduces the effectiveness of anti-diuretic hormone (ADH), a hormone which is meant to slow down your kidneys' excretion of fluid to conserve your precious fluid levels when they are getting low. Drinking a pint of water before going to bed after you have consumed a lot of alcohol can help to reduce the dehydration—and the resulting hangover!

# SHOPPING FOR
# MEALS IN MINUTES

Although this cookbook is excellent for people who just want delicious, nutritious recipes, if you are using it to try to overcome any kind of health problem, you'll need to be well-organised from the start. Most people fail at a special diet because they arrive home tired and hungry, open the fridge and find there's nothing in it that's compatible with the diet. "Oh blow it!" they say, "I'll eat this packet of biscuits and go back on the diet tomorrow." Needless to say, tomorrow may never come.

So before you get cooking, let's look at some of the ingredients you should always have in your fridge or store-cupboard (see panel). If you make sure you don't run out, you will always be able to whip up a delicious meal in minutes. And it's guaranteed to be a lot cheaper than a shop-bought ready meal!

Most of these foods can now be bought in the larger supermarkets as well as in health food shops. Fresh vegetables are cheaper from a greengrocer, and fresh fish from a fishmonger.

If you would like to take advantage of the recipes which use ingredients that you prepare in advance and then freeze to make quick meals later on, a freezer would be a great advantage. And, since one of the best-value sources of protein is the humble dried bean or pea, I am also recommending that you obtain a pressure-cooker. I gave up years ago trying to cook beans, split peas and so on in a normal saucepan. Two hours after starting to boil them they can still be like bullets! In a pressure cooker, even the toughest bean will yield to pressure in 5-10 minutes.

I also like to use a wok (preferably with a see-through lid) for a lot of recipes, but if you cook with electricity, you should substitute a deep frying pan or sauté pan.

## Meals in Minutes Shopping List

See page 22 for sources of unusual items

**Alfalfa seeds**

**Apples**

**Beans (cooked and frozen) or canned in plain water**

**Blueberry or black cherry all-fruit jam**

**Brown rice, cooked and frozen**

**Canned plum tomatoes**

**Carrots**

**Dried fruit**

**Filleted fish for freezing**

**Frozen chopped mixed vegetables**

**Garlic**

**Green cabbage**

**Herbs and spices**

**Lemons or limes**

**Lentils**

**Miso**

**Nuts (almonds, cashews, walnuts, brazils, unsalted peanuts)**

**Oatflakes**

**Olive oil (extra-virgin)**

**Onions**

**Potassium salt**

**Potatoes, especially Desirée or other waxy varieties**

**Prawns**

**Pumpernickel bread (long-life, yeast– and wheat-free)**

**Rice noodles**

**Soya cream**

**Soya, buckwheat, brown rice and polenta flours**

**Sunflower seeds**

**Sweet (bell) peppers**

**Tamari sauce**

**Tofu**

**Tomato purée (paste)**

# PREPARING BROWN RICE AND BEANS FOR THE FREEZER

Defrost and use for recipes which require "cooked rice" or "cooked beans"

## Brown Rice

Brown rice is nuttier than white rice, with a different texture. It contains all the B vitamins which are lost when rice is "polished". You can buy brown rice from supermarkets and health food shops.

Wash well, then pre-soak overnight in twice its volume of filtered water.Use the same water for cooking. Bring to the boil then cover tightly and simmer on the lowest possible heat until tender (20-25 minutes).

If the water has not all been absorbed, drain away the excess (or save it for adding to soup, as it is very rich in vitamins) then leave the rice in the covered saucepan away from the heat for 5 minutes, after which it is ready to serve.

Once cold, brown rice can be spread out on an oiled baking tray, frozen, then crumbled into grains and bagged for the freezer.

## Dried Beans

These should be soaked in water before use. Cover with four times their volume in boiling filtered water and leave overnight.

Throw away the soaking water, place the beans, well covered with fresh water, in a pressure cooker, bring to full steam, and leave on a low-medium heat for 3-10 minutes, depending on size and age. Remove from the heat and place the pressure cooker in a sink of cold water. You cannot open the pressure cooker until it has cooled down enough to reduce the steam pressure inside.

Pressure-cooking breaks down the poisonous lectins found in raw beans. If you do not have a pressure cooker, boil them fast for at least 10 minutes before simmering or slow-cooking.

To freeze, allow to cool and follow the same procedure as for frozen brown rice.

# Maximizing Nutrients

I can't help cringing when I visit someone's kitchen and watch a few handfuls of chopped vegetables rapidly boiling in a huge panful of water.

One of the first rules of cookery is that most of the vitamins from vegetables end up in the cooking water. So the second rule is to keep the cooking water to make soup, sauce or gravy, or to use a cooking method which doesn't need any water. Here are some alternatives to boiling.

## Steaming

This is a good method for potatoes, since only an inch of water is needed in the bottom of the pan. You don't need to buy a special steamer. Cheap metal steaming baskets are available which open up to fit inside any saucepan. You may need to allow the potatoes a few extra minutes' cooking time, and do ensure that the water is kept boiling quite rapidly.

Potato water contains vitamin C and can be saved (or frozen) for adding to soup. In Continental Europe some doctors recommend drinking potato water to help soothe bowel spasms in irritable bowel syndrome. This is because potatoes are related to Belladonna and contain small amounts of atropine-like compounds.

## Braising and Sautées

Braising is a wonderful way to cook vegetables. You just stir vegetable pieces (often with chopped onion for added succulence) into a little hot oil, and then add just a few tablespoons of water before covering the pan very tightly and turning the heat down to the lowest possible setting. The vegetables cook very slowly in their own juices. The result? Delicious!

Sautées are similar but you add more liquid. Once the food is cooked you remove it, reduce the sauce by boiling, and then pour the sauce back over the food.

### STIR-FRYING

This method is very similar to braising, but the vegetables need to be cut into very small pieces or thin strips, and stirred in a large, roomy pan (preferably a Chinese wok) over a high heat until they are part-cooked. A few tablespoons of water are then added to create a lot of steam which helps to soften the vegetables. A lid may then be put over the pan for a short time. Stir-frying is quicker than braising.

### SOUPS

Soups are a wonderful way to get all the goodness out of vegetables, since nothing is thrown away. A thick, chunky soup can be a meal in itself.

### BAKING

Especially if chopped very small (as in a food processor) vegetables can be mixed with chopped nuts and with grains such as brown rice or buckwheat, and then oven-baked. Flavoured with herbs or soya sauce, this deliciously moist dish complements any main item on the menu; or it could be served as a lunchtime snack, on its own or with a sauce.

## Refined Foods

These include

- Foods made from white flour (e.g. bread, pasta, cookies and cake)
- Sugar and syrup of all types
- White (polished) rice
- Most breakfast cereals
- Most cooking oils and margarines.

Foods are refined for various reasons, often to extend their shelf life. Refining means removing part of the food (often the nutrient-rich outer layer) or extracting from the whole food only the part you want (such as sugar or pure oil), leaving up to 90 per cent of the vitamins and minerals behind. The manufacturers may then try to sell you back the wheatgerm or bran removed from the cereals, or the vitamin E extracted from the oils.

By law, refined foods often have to be "fortified" with added vitamins as they are so depleted. Unrefined foods don't need added vitamins since they can be up to ten times more nutritious.

# USING UNFAMILIAR INGREDIENTS

| Ingredient | Where To Get It | What It's Good For | How To Use It |
|---|---|---|---|
| **Alfalfa Sprouts and Seeds** | Sprouts: Health food shops<br>Seeds: Health food shops and garden centres | Rich in coumarin, a substance related to antioxidants known as flavonoids, which helps the lymphatic system | Alfalfa sprouts can be bought in packets, but it is cheaper to make your own. Place a level tablespoon of seeds in a large jar, then cover the jar with a piece of nylon fabric from an old pair of tights and secure the fabric with an elastic band around the neck of the jar. Run some water into the jar, shake to thoroughly wet the seeds, then leave overnight. In the morning, pour the water away, straining it through the nylon cover. Rinse the seeds by pouring in water and immediately straining it out again morning and night, and in a few days you will have a luscious growth of curly green sprouts which can be added to soups or eaten as salad. Eat them when they are about one inch long. You can also follow the same procedure to sprout lentils, mung beans, aduki beans, black buckwheat grains, barley grains, almonds and clover seeds. |
| **Bilberries (a small cousin of the blueberry)** | These grow wild in many areas. May be available in frozen food departments of some larger supermarkets | Rich in flavonoids, vitamin C and minerals | Consume them as they are, or place in an oven-proof casserole dish in a medium oven for 25 minutes or until the fruits split and the juices run. Serve hot or cold, with soya cream, or use in any of the recipes in this book which call for blueberries. Bilberries are not quite as sweet as blueberries. If sweetening is required use a small amount of puréed dates. |
| **Blueberries** | Fresh: supermarkets.<br>Frozen: Ardovries Shearway Ltd (see page 163)<br>Dried: Larger branches of Sainsburys | Rich in flavonoids, vitamin C and minerals | Serve fresh with soya yoghurt, or cook as for bilberries. Should need no sweetening as blueberries are sweeter than bilberries. |

| Ingredient | Where To Get It | What It's Good For | How To Use It |
|---|---|---|---|
| **Brown Rice** | Supermarkets and health food shops | Rich in B vitamins. A good source of protein | Brown rice is nuttier than white rice and has a different texture. Wash thoroughly, then pre-soak overnight in twice its volume of filtered water. Use the same water for cooking. Bring to the boil then cover tightly and simmer on the lowest possible heat until tender (20-25 minutes). If the water has not all been absorbed, drain away the excess (or save it for adding to soup, as it is very rich in vitamins) then leave the rice in the covered saucepan away from the heat for 5 minutes, after which it is ready to serve.<br>Once cold, brown rice can be spread out on an oiled baking tray, frozen, then crumbled into grains and bagged for the freezer. |
| **Buckwheat** | Health food shops | Rich in magnesium and in the flavonoid rutin, which helps to build capillary strength | Buckwheat is a grain unrelated to wheat and is a good alternative for wheat allergy sufferers. Buckwheat flour contains no gluten and is the main ingredient of small Russian pancakes known as blinis.<br>To use as an alternative to rice, toast buckwheat grains in a dry frying pan (skillet) for 10 minutes over a medium heat. Put in a saucepan with twice their volume of water. Bring to the boil and simmer very gently with the lid on for 15-20 minutes, or until the grains are tender. |
| **Chestnut Flour** | Health food shops. Infinity Foods and Windmill Organics (see page 163) | Its sweet taste makes it great for cakes and pastries | See the recipes on pages 108 and 138. |
| **Coconut Oil** | Oriental grocers. KTC (Edibles) Ltd (see page 163) | Does not raise cholesterol levels like butter and other animal fats. Contains lauric acid, which combats the Epstein-Barr virus | Use as a replacement for butter in pastry-making and whenever a hard fat is required.<br>Coconut oil is a solid product but is sold in bottles and jars. If the neck of the bottle is too narrow for you to insert a spoon, melt the oil by placing it in a bowl of hot water, then pour it into an old margarine container before refrigerating it, whereupon it will solidify again. |

| Ingredient | Where To Get It | What It's Good For | How To Use It |
|---|---|---|---|
| **Dried Beans, Split Peas, Chickpeas, Marrowfat Peas, Lentils.** (Also known as pulses or legumes) | Supermarkets, grocers and health food shops | A very cheap source of protein, rich in dietary fibre, B vitamins and minerals | All pulses except lentils should be soaked in water before use. Cover with four times their volume in boiling filtered water and leave overnight. Throw away the soaking water, place the pulses, well covered with fresh water, in a pressure cooker, bring to full steam, and cook for 3-10 minutes, depending on age and hardness. Pressure-cooking breaks down the poisonous lectins found in raw beans. If you do not have a pressure cooker, boil them fast for at least 10 minutes before simmering or slow-cooking. Conventional boiling can take two hours or more to soften them, depending on age and size. To freeze, allow to cool and follow the same procedure as for frozen brown rice. Lentils need no presoaking. Boil for 20-30 minutes in two and a quarter times their volume in water. |
| **Miso** | Darker varieties: Health food shops. Pale varieties: Clearspring or Source Foods (see page 163) | A delicious stock paste made from fermented soya. Lower in sodium than most stock paste, and very rich in vitamins and minerals. Also contains protein | Mix with boiling water and use to make gravy and to flavour soups and stews. One variety of miso is made with wheat, and should be avoided while following the principles of this book. Other types, such as barley miso, are ok. Don't overdo the miso—it does contain salt. Use just enough to get some colour and/or flavour into a dish. |
| **Potassium Baking Powder and Potassium Salt (CardiaSalt)** | At the present time in the UK you can only get these by mail order from Biocare Ltd (see page 163) | For baking and seasoning without the added sodium from the usual products. Also increases valuable potassium | Use in accordance with the manufacturer's directions on the container. Potassium salt is also an ingredient in "Low Salt" products, which typically consist of half to two thirds potassium salt and the rest ordinary sodium salt. These are OK to use in recipes specifying "potassium salt" unless you are on a salt-free diet. |
| **Pumpernickel bread** | Supermarkets, health food shops | Wholegrain rye bread with a sweetish, nutty flavour. Buy a brand which contains no yeast or wheat | Eat with soups and salads, or make into an open sandwich (see pages 50-51). Pumpernickel does contain a very small amount of salt, but this should not be a problem. |

| Ingredient | Where To Get It | What It's Good For | How To Use It |
|---|---|---|---|
| **Rice Vermicelli and Noodles** | Vermicelli: Oriental grocers and supermarkets. Noodles: Oriental grocers and some large supermarkets | A good alternative to noodles made from wheat | Thin rice noodles are about twice the thickness of vermicelli. Pour boiling water over them and soak for 2-3 minutes depending on the product. Rinse immediately in cold water. Larger noodles, which are flat and ribbon-like, are also available and can be used as alternatives. |
| **Sheep's Milk Yoghurt** | Supermarkets | A nice creamy alternative to cow's milk yoghurt | Use as normal yoghurt. |
| **Soya Cream** | Supermarkets and health food shops | A blend of soya protein and oil which can be used as an alternative to dairy single cream | Soya cream is used as a topping for desserts, or can be stirred into soup or gravy to achieve the same effect as single cream. *Look for it under brand names such as Provamel's "Soya Dream" since in the UK, EU officials have told manufacturers to remove the description "soya cream" from the packaging on the grounds that the product contains no dairy produce.* |
| **Soya Flour** | Health food shops | High in protein. Provides all the benefits of soy foods, including protection against prostate cancer and menopausal problems | A few tablespoons of soya flour can often be used as an alternative to eggs in baking because of its high protein content. Excellent in the pancake recipe on page 28. |
| **Soya Milk** | Widely available. You may have to try different brands before you find one you like | Provides all the benefits of soy foods | Use in the same way as cow's milk. Contains less protein, calcium and fat, but a good balance of vitamins and minerals. Some brands are enriched with calcium. Add natural vanilla extract to make it taste like cow's milk. |
| **Soya Yoghurt** | Health food shops. Or make your own, using soya milk and some Sojasun as a starter culture | An alternative to cow's milk yoghurt. Provides all the benefits of soy foods, plus the friendly bacteria found in normal yoghurt | Use as normal yoghurt. *N.B. In the UK it has to be sold under descriptions such as "soya speciality with live ferments" (Sojasun, which is a good thick brand), or Yofu, since EU officials have told manufacturers to remove the description "soya yoghurt" from the packaging on the grounds that the product contains no dairy produce.* |

| Ingredient | Where To Get It | What It's Good For | How To Use It |
|---|---|---|---|
| **Spelt Flour** | Health food shops. Some large supermarkets | An alternative to wholewheat flour, also known as "ancient wheat". Most people who are allergic to wheat are not allergic to spelt | Use exactly as wholewheat flour. You can also buy pasta made from spelt. |
| **Sugar-Free (all-fruit) Jam and Marmalade** | Health food shops. Some larger supermarkets and superstores also sell the excellent St Dalfour brand | All-fruit jams are made using fruit juice as a sweetener. They contain nothing except fruit and juice | Use as normal jam or to sweeten desserts. |
| **Tamari Sauce** | Health food shops | A type of soy sauce, made without using wheat | Use tamari sauce sparingly (since it is salty), to flavour stir-fried dishes. For soups and sauces use wheat-free miso (see above). |
| **Tofu** | Supermarkets and health food shops | A good source of protein made from soy—as good as eating meat but with added health benefits | Many of the recipes in this book use tofu. For best results, use the right type. Get to know a particular brand and stick to it if it works. "Silken" tofu has the consistency of blancmange. It is sold as soft, medium or firm varieties, although the package does not always tell you (a) that the product is silken tofu, or (b) whether it is soft or firm. Silken tofu is best for liquidizing and making into mayonnaise and other creamy products. The firmer it is, the less water it contains, and the more water you may have to add to get the finished consistency you want.<br>Standard tofu can also be soft or firm. It has a "chewier" consistency and is best for cutting into cubes, dusting with brown rice flour and frying in oil. Can be marinated beforehand. It can also be liquidized with a little soya milk or water, poured into moulds, and baked with flavourings. The finished result has a consistency like quiche or omelette.<br>Tofu needs quite a lot of flavouring to make it really nice to eat. |

# Breakfasts

**A**lways eat breakfast, even if you are trying to lose weight. During the night your body slows down its metabolism (burns calories more slowly) to conserve energy. Only when you start eating again does it speed things up. A carbohydrate-only breakfast will leave you feeling hungry again quite quickly, so make sure you include some protein and oils in your breakfast to keep your blood sugar even. Nuts, fish and avocados are ideal.

# Breakfast Corn Pancakes and Waffles

## Ingredients to make 4 pancakes

2 heaped tbsp each of

Finely ground yellow polenta meal

Buckwheat flour

Soya (soy) flour

(adding up to a combined quantity
of about 115 g/4 ounces/½ cup)

250 ml/8½ fluid oz/generous ¾
cup water

## Instructions

Mix the ingredients thoroughly together to form a smooth, runny batter. It should be able to quickly spread to the edges when poured into a pan. Heat a lightly oiled frying pan (skillet) over a medium to high heat. When hot, pour in enough batter to cover the bottom of the pan and quickly tilt the pan so that the batter can run to the edges, forming a pancake shape. Cook for about one minute, or until small holes form and the top is just set. Turn the pancake over with a spatula (or toss it if you're brave!) and cook the other side for about the same time. Oil the pan again and stir the batter before making the next pancake. Stack the pancakes and keep them warm until you are ready to eat them. They are delicious rolled up after spreading with apple butter (see page 130) and cinnamon or ground cardamom, or with all-fruit blueberry jam.

The pancake batter will keep in the fridge for a few days, allowing you to make just one or two pancakes very quickly. Stir well before cooking. I make so many of these pancakes that I pre-mix the flours when I buy them. The mixture consists of one part of each type of flour and is kept in a special jar.

## What It's Good For

Yellow polenta flour is rich in anti-cancer carotenes (substances similar to beta carotene). Buckwheat flour is rich in molybdenum - a mineral needed by the liver for detoxification work. Soya flour is a rich source of hormone-balancing isoflavones which help to prevent problems relating to excess or insufficient oestrogen, and excess testosterone (a male hormone related to oestrogen). According to scientific studies a diet rich in soya flour and other soya products helps to prevent all kinds of problems, from menopausal hot flushes, to breast cancer

NB: Waffles use more pancake batter than pancakes.

**Waffles**

Make a thicker batter, using less water, and spoon it into an oiled, preheated waffle iron. Cook for 2-3 minutes. Turn the waffle upside-down before serving if the pattern does not come out well on the top, and spread with all-nut peanut, cashew or almond butter and/or all-fruit blueberry jam or orange marmalade.

and prostate cancer. In clinical trials women with menopausal symptoms have reversed them by eating a diet rich in soya flour.

# Yoghurt with Almonds and Apple Compote

**Makes one serving**

Sheep's (and cow's) yoghurt has a sharper flavour than soya yoghurt.

**Instructions**

Swirl 4 tbsp sheep's milk or soya yoghurt into a generous serving of apple sauce (see page 130).

Sprinkle liberally with toasted flaked almonds.

*Variations*

Prunes soaked in water overnight and gently poached until tender also go well with yoghurt.

## What It's Good For

Both sheep's and soya yoghurts are rich in protein. It's a good idea to start your day with some protein because this is the time of day when your body can best assimilate it.

Protein is also more filling than carbohydrate. An all-carbohydrate breakfast can leave you feeling hungry again within two hours.

# Authentic Swiss Muesli with Flaked Nuts and Sweet Apricots

## Ingredients for one serving

3 tbsp medium or fine ground
oatmeal

Water

Soya or almond milk* to taste

1 tbsp flaked nuts

1 unsulphured dried apricot,
chopped small

*See page 147

Dried apricots are orange in colour
if treated with sulphur dioxide. This
additive is an intestinal irritant and
can cause bloating and gas.
Unsulphured apricots (from health
food shops) are dark brown and
much sweeter in flavour.

## Instructions

Did you know that the Swiss never eat muesli straight out of the packet? They know that raw grains should always be soaked (or cooked) before eating them, because this breaks down mildly poisonous chemicals they contain, known as enzyme inhibitors, that can upset your intestines.

Soak the oatmeal overnight in water. The amount of water you need will depend on how much the oatmeal can absorb—about three times its volume for medium oatmeal, and more for fine oatmeal. If you find after an hour or so that the mixture has become too solid, add more water. No milk is necessary since the oats create their own milk. In the morning check the consistency and add a little soya or nut milk if you wish, to achieve your preferred consistency. If you use fine oatmeal, the result will be very creamy. Stir in the dried apricot pieces and sprinkle with flaked nuts.

## What It's Good For

Oats and oatmeal are one of the best possible sources of magnesium and B vitamins. These nutrients are often lacking in diets which rely on convenience foods. A magnesium deficiency can reduce your liver's ability to get rid of toxins, and can be responsible for a lot of the symptoms listed on page 9, especially those related to anxiety and stress. Magnesium is rapidly used up in stress situations. Muscles have difficulty in relaxing when they are short of magnesium.

# Fried Herring Cakes

## Ingredients for 2 servings

2 medium herrings, scaled, trimmed and gutted

2 tbsp olive oil

2 dessertspoons chick pea (gram) flour

Potassium salt

Freshly ground black pepper

## Instructions

Poach the herrings in a few tablespoons of water in a lidded pan over a low heat for ten minutes, until the fish comes apart easily. Allow the fish to cool, then slit it open lengthwise and carefully remove all the bones.

Using a fork, mash the fish with the chick pea flour and seasonings, then, using your hands, divide it into four balls and form each ball into a fairly thin patty. Dust the outside of the patties with more chick pea flour.

Heat the oil in a frying pan (skillet) over a fairly high heat, then put the patties into the pan and fry for 1-2 minutes on each side or until brown. The patties can be prepared the night before for cooking in the morning.

Serve hot with home-made tomato ketchup (see page 137).

You could also serve these herring cakes cold as a starter, on a bed of shredded lettuce with lemon wedges. Or tuck them into a folded round of unleavened bread and top with salad ingredients and a squeeze of lemon juice.

## What It's Good For

Herrings are rich in omega 3 oils which help to protect us against heart attacks. They discourage our red blood cells from clumping together and so blocking our arteries. If foods were priced according to how healthy they are to eat, few of us would be able to afford herrings. As it is, they are probably the best value fish you can get, and are very beautiful with their shiny, silvery scales. Herrings are also an excellent source of zinc. A zinc deficiency can lead to skin and immunity problems, a poor sense of taste or smell, and to prostate problems in older men.

# Sultana and Sunflower Seed Porridge with Milk and Cream

## What It's Good For

See page 30 for the benefits of oats and oatmeal.

Sunflower seeds are rich in essential polyunsaturated oils, calcium, magnesium and methionine, which is normally a constituent of animal protein and is generally not found in large amounts in plant foods. Methionine is turned into glutathione in your liver, which, together with the trace element selenium, makes an important free radical fighting enzyme known as glutathione peroxidase. Unlike animal fats, the omega 6 oils in natural sunflower seeds are very beneficial to health.

### Ingredients for one serving

250 ml/9 fluid oz/generous ¾ cup soya (soy) milk

3 tbsp rolled oats or medium oatmeal

2 tsp raisins

2 tsp sunflower seeds

Soya (soy) cream

### Special Tip

Add a few drops of natural vanilla extract to soya milk to make it taste more like cow's milk. Vanilla is very similar to coumarin, a substance which gives cow's milk its flavour of new-mown hay. Coumarin actually comes from new-mown hay.

### Instructions

Put the milk and oats in a small, heavy-bottomed saucepan (enamelled cast iron if you have one) over a medium heat.

Bring to the boil, stirring constantly, then turn down the heat to a simmer and add the raisins and sunflower seeds.

Keep stirring for a minute or two until it thickens. Add a little more soya milk if you prefer a more runny porridge. Serve with a little soya cream poured over the top.

This is a delicious and satisfying breakfast, especially on a cold winter's day. If you prefer extra sweetness, use a variety of soya milk which has been sweetened with a little apple juice.

This recipe takes only 5 minutes to make.

# Granola

## Ingredients for 2 servings

<u>6 tbsp rolled oats</u>

<u>3 tbsp chopped mixed nuts</u>

<u>2 tbsp sunflower seeds</u>

<u>1 tbsp groundnut oil</u>

<u>1 tbsp raisins</u>

<u>1 tbsp unsulphured dried apricots, diced</u>

<u>A few drops of natural vanilla extract</u>

## Instructions

Mix all the ingredients except the dried fruit thoroughly together.

Put a dry frying pan (skillet) over a low heat. When hot, add the ingredients and cook for 20 minutes, stirring occasionally.

Remove from the heat and stir in the dried fruit. Once cool, store in an airtight container.

To serve, pour into a bowl and add soya milk. You could also add prunes, apple compote or fresh fruit such as bananas, pears or strawberries.

## What It's Good For

This delicious, very nutty cereal can be eaten for breakfast or as a snack at any time of day. See pages 30 and 32 for the benefits of oats and sunflower seeds. Dried fruit is very rich in the mineral potassium. Groundnut oil has been used in this recipe because it has to be heated. Like olive oil, groundnut oil contains mainly monounsaturated fatty acids, which are less easily damaged by heat than most other oils. Groundnut oil also has little flavour of its own, and so is ideal for recipes like this.

# Avocado Smoothie with Banana and Strawberries

## Ingredients for 2 servings

One avocado pear

600 ml/1 pint/2 cups soya milk

Half a banana, sliced roughly

One handful of sweet strawberries

1 tsp natural vanilla extract

## Instructions

Probably the fastest breakfast in the universe!

Open the avocado and remove the stone. Cut the flesh into 8 pieces.

Liquidize all the ingredients together and drink immediately.

Small, ripe avocados with a good flavour are best for this recipe. Liquidized avocado turns brown quickly, so don't let this hang around before drinking it.

## What It's Good For

Described as one of nature's most perfect foods, creamy, buttery avocado pears are so nutritious that they are practically a whole meal in themselves. They are rich in protein, omega 6 polyunsaturated oils, vitamin B6 and other B vitamins, vitamin E, iron and copper, and provide three times as much potassium as bananas. They are also easy to digest.

The rough-skinned Hass avocado has a particularly good flavour.

The protein in this drink will help to keep you going until lunchtime.

# Lunches, Suppers Snacks and Starters

The new way to serve a family meal or a dinner for guests is a "buffet meal". It's similar to a high tea - the traditional mix and match evening meal in Northern England - or to a Chinese or Ukrainian meal, where people help themselves from a variety of hot or cold dishes.

Try arranging a selection of the following dishes in the centre of the dining table:

- Eggplant Caviar (page 37)
- Frittata with Ginger and Courgettes (page 38)
- Potato Wedges Roasted with Olive Oil and Garlic (page 40)
- Guacamole (page 52)
- Falafel (page 54)
- Mini rainbow salads (page 102)
- German potato salad (page 100)
- Pumpernickel, and rye crispbread.

Or put out the ingredients for Danish Open Sandwiches (see pages 50 and 51) and let people build their own.

And of course buffets are great for parties and the cold items for packed lunches too!

# Russian Borscht

## Ingredients for 6-8 servings

1.7 litres/3 pints/6 cups water

¼ head small to medium green cabbage, coarsely shredded

2 medium potatoes, cut into four lengthwise, then thinly sliced

3 medium beetroot (beets), boiled whole, peeled, cooled and coarsely grated

2 medium carrots, coarsely grated

1 medium onion

1 small can tomato purée (paste)

4 cloves garlic, peeled

2 tbsp extra virgin olive oil

Potassium salt

## Instructions

Put the potatoes and shredded cabbage in a large saucepan with the water and potassium salt and bring to the boil. Simmer for 15 minutes then add the grated carrot and simmer for a further 5 minutes.

Meanwhile cut the onion into 8 pieces and process with the garlic cloves in a food processor with the "S" blade.

Heat the oil in a stir-fry pan or sauté pan, and stir the onion and garlic mixture over a medium heat until softened but not brown.

When the cabbage, potato and carrot are tender, stir in the tomato purée then add the softened onion and garlic mixture, followed by the grated beetroot. Gently heat through until just simmering, then serve in bowls topped with a dollop of sour cream (see page 128).

## What It's Good For

Beetroot is a wonderful herb-like food which stimulates your liver and gall bladder to drain off toxins into your intestines, so that they can be released in a bowel movement. It works a bit like pulling the plug out when a sink is full of dirty water.
Cabbage is a great anti-cancer vegetable, since it helps your liver to process toxins into more harmless substances. It is also rich in a powerful antioxidant flavonoid known as quercetin which has been found to help prevent cataracts and allergic problems. Use the darkest green cabbage you can find.

# Eggplant Caviar

## Ingredients for 2-4 servings

1 medium aubergine (eggplant), washed and dried

1 small onion, finely chopped in a food processor

2 medium tomatoes, skinned, deseeded and roughly chopped

2 tbsp lemon juice

Extra virgin olive oil

1 tbsp parsley, finely chopped

Potassium salt

Black pepper

Parsley or coriander leaf (cilantro) to garnish

## Instructions

Steam the aubergine whole (or cut in half to fit the pan) for 15 minutes until soft. Sweat the onion over a medium heat for 5 minutes with 2 tbsp olive oil. When the aubergine is ready, dice it finely and add it to the pan with the onions. Stir, cover the pan and continue cooking very gently for another 5 minutes, then turn off the heat. Stir in the chopped tomatoes, parsley, potassium salt and pepper, lemon juice and another tablespoon of olive oil. Mix and incorporate thoroughly. Allow to cool, then chill and garnish with a sprig of parsley or coriander (cilantro) before serving on a bed of shredded iceberg lettuce. Serve as part of a buffet meal (see page 35) or put teaspoonfuls on cucumber slices or pieces of toasted (not fried) poppadom, or on small squares of wheat- and yeast-free pumpernickel bread and top with a dollop of sour cream (see page 128).

This dish is better if made the day before and kept cool before serving.

*Variation*

Can also be made with raw onion or spring onion (scallion) instead of cooked.

## What It's Good For

Russians really do eat this dish, and call it caviar. Many prefer it to the real thing. Aubergine is a rich source of flavonoids, and can help to lower cholesterol. It is also known as eggplant because of its creamy texture when cooked.

Please note that aubergines do not contain "bitter juices" and do not need to be treated with salt before cooking. If you throw away their juice you will throw away a lot of their nutritional value.

# Frittata (Italian Omelette) with Ginger and Courgettes

## Ingredients for 6 servings

115 g/4 ounces/½ cup chick pea
   (gram) flour, sieved

250 ml/9 fluid oz/1 cup water

1 medium courgette (zucchini) fairly
   thinly sliced

4 spring onions (scallions) including
   the green part, very thinly
   sliced

4 cloves garlic, finely chopped

1 tbsp finely grated fresh ginger

Extra virgin olive oil

### Tip

Cut any hard bits off a big piece of
ginger then grate it all and freeze
teaspoonfuls in the individual wells
of ice cube trays. (The skin is so
delicate you don't need to peel it.)

## Instructions

Stir the water into the gram flour a little at a time, until it is all
incorporated and the mixture is smooth. Stir in the grated
ginger. Don't be alarmed at how watery the mixture is—it will
puff up nicely.

Fry the courgette slices in 2-3 tbsp olive oil over a medium heat on each side for 2 minutes until golden, using a
frying pan (skillet) with a 9½ inch diameter. Remove from the
pan, then add the onion and garlic. Stir and fry gently for 2
minutes until soft but not brown. Replace the courgettes in
the pan and arrange the contents of the pan evenly over the
bottom. Give the gram flour, ginger and water mixture a final
stirring, then pour it carefully into the hot frying pan. Scram-
ble the ingredients at the bottom of the pan very gently and
briefly with a spoon, then cover the pan tightly and leave
over a low to moderate heat for 15 minutes, until the sides
and bottom of the frittata are golden brown and the top is set.

Slide the frittata on to a large plate, put another plate
over the top, invert, then slide the frittata back into the frying
pan to cook the other side for 5 minutes.

Serve the frittata warm or cold, cut into wedges and garnished with watercress.

## What It's Good For

Gram (chick pea) flour is
very rich in protein, and in
this dish makes a
delicious replacement for
eggs, which are normally
used to make frittata (a
type of thick, round
omelette).
It is also a good source of
many other nutrients,
including calcium,
magnesium, iron, copper
and some of the B
vitamins.
Ginger is a wonderful aid
to digestion. In Chinese
medicine it is considered
to warm the circulation
and to combat catarrh and
bronchitis.

# Detoxification Soup

## Ingredients for 6 servings

1.7 litres/3 pints/6 cups water

225 g/½ lb white fish, cut into chunks

1 long, white (mooli) radish, cut into matchsticks

1 medium onion, chopped

2 boiled, peeled beetroot (beets), diced

225 g/½ lb brussels sprouts, sliced

1 bunch watercress, chopped

1 small can of tomato purée (paste)

2 tbsp extra virgin olive oil

1 tbsp gelatine

2 tsp turmeric (yellow oriental spice)

1 tsp Glaubers Salts (sodium sulphate - ask your pharmacist)

## Instructions

Sweat the chopped onion gently in the olive oil, in the bottom of a large saucepan. When softened, stir in the turmeric until it is thoroughly incorporated. Pour in the water and bring almost to the boil. When nearly boiling, remove from the heat, sprinkle in the gelatine powder and whisk until dissolved, then stir in the Glaubers salts and tomato purée. Finally, add the fish and vegetables, except the beetroot.

Bring back to the boil and simmer gently for 20 minutes. Gently stir in the diced beetroot and serve.

## What It's Good For

This recipe is primarily intended as a medicine. It contains four sets of ingredients to help your liver clear toxins from your blood:
**Brussels sprouts**
**Protein**
**Glycine (gelatine)**
**Inorganic sulphate (Glaubers salts)**
help it process toxins.
**Quercetin (onions)**
**Vitamin C (brussels sprouts)**
help neutralise toxic free radicals produced in your liver as it works.
**Radish, beetroot and watercress**
help drain toxins out of your liver and gallbladder into your intestines, ready for removal via your stools.
**Turmeric**
helps protect your liver cells against attacks from toxins.

# Potato Wedges Roasted with Olive Oil and Garlic

### Ingredients for each serving

1 medium potato, scrubbed

1 clove garlic, chopped

2 tbsp extra virgin olive oil

1 tsp potassium salt

Cayenne pepper

### Instructions

Preheat the oven to 200°C/400°F/gas mark 6.

Pound the chopped garlic with the salt until smooth, using a mortar and pestle, then stir in the olive oil and cayenne pepper. Put this mixture in a shallow, oven-proof dish large enough to hold the potato wedges.

Bring one inch of water to the boil in a saucepan with a steamer basket.

Leave the skins on the potatoes. Cut each potato into half lengthwise and each half into four long wedges. Put the potato wedges in the steamer and steam over a medium heat for five minutes. Remove the wedges and brush each one with the oil and garlic mixture, ensuring it is thoroughly coated.

Arrange the wedges peeled side down in the dish and roast for 30 minutes. Baste after 15 minutes by dipping a basting brush into the oil, and brushing the wedges with it before returning the dish to the oven.

Serve as a snack dipped in hummus (page 41) or eggplant caviar (page 37).

### What It's Good For

Potatoes are rich in potassium and many other nutrients. They also contain a small amount of vitamin C. Cooking them in this way, with a little olive oil, is an excellent way to make them crunchy and get all their goodness without the excessive fat of deep-frying.

# Hummus

## Ingredients for 4 servings

In this recipe a cup means an ordinary teacup

1½ cups freshly cooked chick peas (still warm)*

½ cup cooking liquid from the chick peas

2 heaped tbsp sesame seeds

4 tbsp extra virgin olive oil

1 tbsp lemon juice

1 clove garlic, crushed

½ tsp potassium salt

Cayenne pepper to taste

*See page 19

## Instructions

Blend all the ingredients together in a food processor, adding more cooking liquid if necessary, until the mixture achieves the consistency of a thick dip.

Use as a dip for crudités (page 60) or roast potato wedges (page 40) or combine with alfalfa sprouts (page 22), peanuts, green pepper strips and grated radish and tuck into a folded round of unleavened bread (page 134).

## What It's Good For

Chick peas are very rich in protein, and are also a good source of many other nutrients, including calcium, magnesium, iron, copper and some of the B vitamins.
Sesame seeds are one of the best available sources of calcium and magnesium, and also provide protein and zinc. They are one of the few good plant sources of the amino acid methionine. Research shows that they can help to lower cholesterol levels in the body.

# Plum and Spring Onion Sushi

## Ingredients to make 32 pieces

2 sheets of nori* approx 19x20 cm/7½x8 inches, cut in half

Approx 16 tbsp short-grain brown rice boiled for an extra 5 minutes until it is a little sticky

4 ready-to-eat (firm) prunes which have been marinaded for 2 hours in 3 tbsp tamari sauce and 1 tbsp rice wine vinegar (or cider vinegar)

2 spring onions (scallions), cut into 1-inch segments then finely shredded lengthwise

1 tsp wasabi sauce or ½ tsp wasabi powder

*Thin but strong and flexible sheets of pressed seaweed. It can be bought from health food stores or by mail order from Clearspring (see page 163).

## Instructions

Remove the prunes from the marinade, cut them into thin strips, and mix the wasabi with the rest of the marinade.

Place a half-sheet of nori on a clean tea towel, with the long edge towards you, and spread 2 tbsp of the cooked rice in a line along the centre from left to right. Lay a quarter of the prune strips on top of the rice followed by a quarter of the spring onion shreds. Carefully spread 2 more tbsp of rice over the top. Sprinkle with some of the marinade.

Now press the rice mixture down as firmly as you can with a fork. Roll the nori around the filling just like pastry round a sausage roll. Moisten one edge so that the edge of the nori will stick to the other edge. It may take a little practice to get the quantity of rice filling just right so that it all fits in the nori sheet.

Put the sushi roll to one side, resting on its seam, while you make the others. When you are ready to serve the sushi, cut the roll into 8 or more bite-sized segments, using a very sharp knife.

### Alternative filling

Sticky rice plus cucumber and cooked carrot strips flavoured with umeboshi plum sauce (from Clearspring, page 163).

## What It's Good For

Like most seafood, seaweed is rich in iodine, a trace mineral needed by your thyroid gland. Iodine is no longer routinely added to salt (at least in the UK) and most people get it from dairy produce; iodine is used to sterilize the teats of cows before they are milked! An iodine deficiency is linked with higher rates of breast cancer and other breast diseases. Japanese women, who eat a diet very rich in iodine (including sushi) have always had a very low rate of breast cancer. Iodine deficiency may also be responsible for a type of nerve damage which leads to hearing

# Miniature Baked Omelettes with Four Fillings

## Ingredients for 4 servings

1 x 250 g pack/8½ ounces/generous 1 cup
    standard firm tofu

4 tbsp soya milk

Tamari sauce

Potassium salt & freshly ground black pepper

**For the parsley and mushroom filling**

3 medium white mushrooms, finely chopped
    and fried in a little olive oil for 1-2 minutes

1 tsp fresh, finely chopped parsley

**For the shallot filling**

1 medium shallot, finely diced and gently fried
    in olive oil until soft but not brown.

**For the carrot, ginger and seaweed
filling**

1 tbsp carrot grated into fine shreds

2 inch square piece of nori seaweed

1 tsp fresh grated ginger

**For the sun-dried tomato and basil
filling**

3 large basil leaves, finely shredded

1 medium piece sun-dried tomato, finely
    shredded

## Instructions

Preheat the oven to 200°C/400°F/gas mark 6, and oil 12 wells of a mini-muffin tin.

Toast the nori sheet quickly under a hot grill (broiler) until it lightens in colour and turns crispy. Break into small pieces.

Using the S-blade of your food processor, whizz the tofu with the soya milk, potassium salt and a few dashes of tamari sauce until creamy-smooth. This may take a few minutes. Scrape down the sides with a spatula from time to time.

Divide the mixture equally between four small bowls. To each bowl, add the ingredients for each of the fillings, plus a little black pepper, and stir together well.

Using two teaspoons, drop the mixture in the wells of the oiled mini-muffin tin and smooth down the surface. Bake in the oven for 20-25 minutes or until firm and springy and beginning to turn golden on top. Serve hot or cold on a bed of shredded lettuce, with some fruit chutney.

## What It's Good For

The main ingredient in this recipe is tofu, a protein-rich soya product. See page 28 for some of the health benefits of soy. Unlike ordinary omelettes, this recipe is low in saturated fat but the taste and texture is remarkably like the real thing. Try inventing some more fillings of your own.

# Speciality Pâtés

## The Basic Mixture

**Makes 4 Servings**

115 g/4 ounces/½ cup dried
butterbeans (lima beans)

75 ml cold-pressed, unrefined
sunflower oil

## Instructions

Cover the beans with four times their volume in boiling water and leave to soak overnight. Drain and place in a pressure cooker over a high heat with plenty of water to cover the beans generously. Put the lid on and bring the pressure cooker up to full steam. Cook for 6 to 10 minutes, depending on the age of the beans, then turn off the heat and immediately plunge the base of the pressure cooker into a sink of cold water. Once the pressure has reduced and you can open the lid, check that the beans are soft and tender by eating one. Do not allow the beans to become cold before you carry out the next stage.

Transfer the warm beans to a food processor. Using the S blade, process them with the sunflower oil until smooth and creamy. This may take several minutes. Scrape the sides down with a rubber spatula from time to time.

This basic mixture is flavoured by adding other ingredients

- Either to the food processor while blending
- Or to the oil, to flavour it before processing it with the beans
- Or to the finished product, by mashing them in roughly.

## What It's Good For

The basic ingredients of these pâtés are butterbeans (lima beans) and sunflower oil. Like all pulses or legumes (members of the bean and lentil family), they are rich in protein, especially in the protein constituent lysine, an amino acid which is hard to get from other plant foods. Try to use a cold-pressed, unrefined sunflower oil rather than supermarket oils, which are usually bleached and chemically treated to improve their shelf life. When using unrefined oils, make sure they are as fresh as possible since they do not keep as well as chemically treated oils.

# Poached Salmon and Dill Pâté

## Ingredients for 4 servings

1 quantity of basic pâté mix

60 g/2 ounces fresh filleted salmon

1 tsp fresh dill, chopped

2 tsp fresh lemon juice

Potassium salt

Freshly ground black pepper

## Instructions

Stir the lemon juice and seasoning into the basic pâté mix and incorporate thoroughly. Poach the fish in a few tablespoons of water for 5 minutes in a small covered pan. The salmon is cooked when it flakes easily. Drain the salmon and flake it, then mash it roughly into the basic pâté mix together with the chopped dill.

# Mushroom and Garlic Pâté

## Ingredients for 4 servings

One quantity of basic pâté mix

115 g/4 ounces/1 cup mushrooms, chopped

½ clove garlic, chopped

Extra virgin olive oil

Tamari sauce

Freshly ground black pepper

## Instructions

Use mushrooms which have developed some black gills, as this helps to give this pâté a good colour.

Fry the chopped mushrooms in olive oil until golden. Whizz the mushrooms and garlic with the pâté mix and a few dashes of tamari sauce in a food processor until smooth. Stir in the black pepper.

## How to serve the Speciality Pâtés

Spread on pumpernickel, rice cakes, oatcakes or wheat-free rye crispbreads such as Ryvita.

Mix with salad ingredients such as alfalfa sprouts, spread on warm pancakes (see page 28) and roll up like a Swiss roll. Keep warm until ready to serve.

Make canapés by squeezing the pâté from an icing bag on to cucumber slices. Top with half an olive.

Make polenta as described on page 94. When you pour the polenta out of the saucepan, spread it out in a well-oiled large dish or

# Italian Herb Pâté

**Ingredients for 4 servings**

1 quanity of basic pâté mix

2 tbsp finely chopped fresh basil or
  pesto sauce (page 101)

Potassium salt

Freshly ground black pepper

**Instructions**

Whizz these ingredients together in a food processor.

# Garlic, Chilli and Tomato Pâté

**Ingredients for 4 servings**

One quantity of basic pâté mix

1 tbsp tomato purée (paste)

½ clove garlic

½ tsp cayenne pepper

Potassium salt

**Instructions**

Stir the ingredients together until thoroughly incorporated.

tray so that it makes only a thin layer (¼-½ inch thick). Smooth this layer to ensure it is as even as possible. When cold, cut out small rounds of polenta with a pastry cutter, fry in hot olive oil until golden, then top with pâté and a sprinkling of fresh herbs or finely diced sweet peppers. Serve immediately.

Fill ramekin dishes with the pâtés and serve as a starter for spreading on crudités (pieces of raw carrot, celery, radish etc.). The pâtés are liable to discolour slightly if left exposed for too long. You cannot entirely prevent this but it helps to whizz a tablespoon of fresh lemon juice into the basic mix.

# Delicious Dips

You can also make dips with your basic pâté mix. Serve these with:

- Pieces of toasted (not fried) poppadom
- Crudités (carrot and celery sticks, radishes etc.—page 60)
- Corn chips
- Potato wedges (page 40)
- As a dressing for salads
- As a topping for baked potatoes.

## Avocado Dip

**Ingredients for 4 servings**

1 quanity of basic pâté mix

1 avocado pear, roughly chopped

2 tsp fresh lemon juice

Freshly ground black pepper

**Instructions**

Whizz all the ingredients together in a food processor until smooth.

## Carrot and Coriander Dip

**Ingredients for 4 servings**

One quantity of basic pâté mix

2 tbsp coriander (cilantro) leaves, finely chopped

½ tsp cayenne pepper

Potassium salt

**Instructions**

Stir the ingredients together until thoroughly incorporated.

## Try Some Ideas of Your Own

Lots of vegetables can be used to make delicious dips. Broccoli is especially delicious. Just peel the stem of a small head of broccoli, cut into small pieces and separate the head into small florets. Then steam until tender and whizz into the basic pâté mix. Try it with olives, onions or shallots, asparagus, artichokes, or roasted sweet peppers. Add herbs and spices to taste. Dips are made using added ingredients with a fairly high water content and are therefore softer than pâtés.

# Spiced Bean Röstis

## Ingredients for 2 servings

225 g/½ lb/1 cup cooked black-eyed beans (see page 19)

½ small onion, finely chopped or grated

3 medium-sized starchy (i.e. non-waxy) potatoes

½ tbsp thick soya yoghurt (such as Sojasun brand)

½ tsp curry powder

Olive oil

Potassium salt

Ground black pepper

## Instructions

Peel and grate the potatoes, putting the gratings into a bowl of cold water. Mash the beans thoroughly and mix or blend in a food processor with the remaining ingredients except the olive oil and potato. Form the bean mixture into 4 patties. Using your hands, squeeze out the excess water from the grated potato and lay it on a clean tea towel. Fold the tea towel over and press the potatoes again to dry them as much as possible. Put the grated potatoes on a large plate. Place the bean patties on top of the potatoes, and press down gently. Cover the tops of the potatoes with as much grated potato as you can and press gently again. The potato will create quite a ragged covering, but this will adhere to the mixture when you start to cook the patties. Put a heavy-bottomed frying pan (skillet) over a moderate heat and add a few tbsp olive oil. Slide a spatula under each rösti to transfer it to the pan, and cook for about 5 minutes each side or until the potato is brown and crisp. Serve immediately with a mixed salad and a spoonful of Cacik (page 136) or Garlic Crème (page 129).

*Recipe by Carolyn Gibbs*

## What It's Good For

These little Röstis are delicious and packed with protein from the beans. (Leftover basic pâté mix works just as well). Beans are rich in an amino acid known as lysine, which is needed for energy production and is lacking in most plant foods. In the human body, lysine is also converted into carnitine, an amino acid which helps to transport fat and convert it into energy.
Vegetarians and vegans should eat beans and lentils regularly to avoid developing a lysine deficiency.

# Creamy Butternut Soup

## Ingredients for 4 servings

1 medium butternut squash

1 litre/1¾ pints/4 cups soya (soy) milk

1 large onion, finely chopped

2 tbsp extra virgin olive oil

Freshly ground black pepper

## Instructions

Preheat the oven to 180°C/350°F/gas mark 4.

Cut the squash in half lengthwise, and remove the seeds with a spoon. Lay the squash pieces cut side down on a greased baking tray and bake in the pre-heated oven for 30 minutes or until soft.

Meanwhile sweat the onion in the olive oil in a large, heavy-bottomed saucepan over a low heat.

When the squash is ready, peel off the outside skin, chop the flesh and add it to the pan of onions, stir and heat through then add the soya milk. Bring almost to the boil, stirring from time to time.

Using a hand blender, whizz the ingredients together until smooth and creamy.

If you find the soup a little too thick, you can add some water to correct the consistency.

Reheat if necessary, stir in some freshly ground black pepper and serve immediately. I find that this soup does not need any salt, but you can add a little potassium salt if you wish.

## What It's Good For

Like carrots and orange sweet potatoes, butternut squash are rich in cancer-preventing carotenes. The best thing about this soup is that it tastes like something made with lavish amounts of cream, yet it is quite low in calories.

# Danish Open Sandwiches (Smørrebrød)

Open sandwiches are made with only one slice of bread (in this case pumpernickel), piled high with delicacies, and eaten with a knife and fork. Prepare ingredients according to how many people you are catering for.

## Salmon and Potato Salad Topping

### Ingredients

Wheat- and yeast-free
   pumpernickel bread*

Fresh salmon, filleted

Potato salad (see page 100) made
   with finely diced potatoes

Mayonnaise (see page 132)

Cucumber, finely diced

Dried dill herb

*This is a black rye bread with a strong, sweet flavour, ideal for open sandwiches. It is easily available from supermarkets and delicatessens.

### Instructions

Poach the salmon fillet by putting it in a small saucepan with a few tablespoons of water and cooking with the lid on for about 10 minutes over a gentle heat until the fish is opaque throughout and flakes easily.

Remove the fish with a slotted spoon and allow to cool. Separate into large flakes. Gently fold the salmon flakes into the potato salad.

Spread a spoonful of mayonnaise on to a slice of pumpernickel, then add a large dollop of the potato salad and salmon mixture. Cover with a tablespoon of diced cucumber and finish with a sprinkling of chopped chives.

*Recipe by Carolyn Gibbs*

## What It's Good For

Dianne Onstad's *Whole Foods Companion* tells us that the basic bread of mediaeval Britain consisted of coarsely ground rye and pea flours, sometimes with a little barley flour mixed in. Nowadays rye is most popular in Russia, as it tolerates the severe climate better than other grains. Wholegrain rye is rich in B vitamins, magnesium, iron and zinc, and its fibre absorbs water well, making it especially good for bowel health. Black rye breads are made by cooking the bread at a relatively low temperature for a long time.

# Hummus and Rainbow Salad Topping

## Ingredients

Wheat- and yeast-free
    pumpernickel bread*

Hummus (see page 41)

Baby new potatoes

Mayonnaise

Gherkins, drained, well-rinsed and
    finely sliced

Grated carrot

Grated raw beetroot

Cherry tomatoes, sliced

Red sweet (bell) pepper, very finely
    diced

Yellow sweet (bell) pepper, very
    finely diced

Lettuce leaves, finely shredded

Spring onion (scallion), finely sliced

Fresh flat-leaf parsley, chopped

*See note on previous page

## Instructions

Steam the baby new potatoes in their jackets until tender. Allow them to cool, then cut them into slices about ¼ inch thick.

Spread a generous layer of hummus on a slice of pumpernickel. Cover with a layer of sliced potato then spread with mayonnaise. Follow with sliced gherkins, grated carrot and beetroot, cherry tomato slices and a sprinkling of the diced peppers. Finish with a little shredded lettuce and a sprinkling of spring onion and chopped parsley.

If you are only making a couple of sandwiches, you may want to cut down on the number of different ingredients, since only a tiny amount of each one will be needed.

*Recipe by Carolyn Gibbs*

Why not make up some open sandwich toppings of your own? The Speciality Pâtés (pages 44-46) and Crab Terrine (page 58) also make a delicious base and can be topped with chopped gherkins, capers, spring onion, (scallion), pickled garlic, alfalfa sprouts (see page 22) and Sour Cream (page 128) or Garlic Crème (page 129).

# Guacamole

## Ingredients for 2-4 servings

1 small, ripe avocado

1 medium tomato, skinned, deseeded and finely chopped

½ green chilli pepper (seeds removed), very thinly sliced

2 tbsp mayonnaise (see page 132)

1 tbsp fresh lemon juice

½ clove garlic, crushed

Potassium salt

## Instructions

Scoop the flesh out of the avocado and, using a fork, immediately mash the lemon juice into it.

Keep mashing until no large lumps remain, then stir in the crushed garlic and potassium salt until thoroughly incorporated, followed by the mayonnaise and then the chopped tomato and chilli pepper.

Serve as a starter or as part of a buffet meal, with tortilla chips or wheat-free crispbread or crackers to dip in the guacamole, or put spoonfuls on to little squares of warm unleavened bread (see page 134).

## What It's Good For

Described as one of nature's most perfect foods, creamy, buttery avocado pears are so nutritious that they are practically a whole meal in themselves. They are rich in protein, omega 6 polyunsaturated oils, vitamin B6 and other B vitamins, vitamin E, iron and copper, and provide three times as much potassium as bananas. They are also easy to digest.

The rough-skinned Hass avocado has a particularly good flavour.

The raw garlic in this recipe is excellent for people with candidiasis and other intestinal infections.

# French Onion Soup

## Ingredients for 2 servings

2 medium onions, peeled, cut in half vertically then thinly sliced

2 tbsp extra virgin olive oil

560 ml/1 pint/2 cups boiling water

1 heaped tbsp wheat-free miso

Herbs to taste: thyme, bay leaves and parsley are all suitable

Freshly ground black pepper

## Instructions

Heat the oil in a large saucepan over a medium heat, then add the onions and stir-fry for about 20 minutes until beginning to caramelize.

Add the water followed by the miso and the herbs. Stir well to dissolve the miso.

Bring the liquid back to the boil, cover, and simmer over a low heat for 30 minutes. Season with freshly-ground black pepper before serving.

## What It's Good For

The therapeutic value of the humble onion is often forgotten in favour of its famous cousin garlic. Onions are a rich source of the so-called "anti-allergy" flavonoid quercetin. This flavonoid is very similar to the drug disodium chromoglycate, which is given to allergy sufferers to switch off their symptoms. Like the drug, quercetin has the ability to inhibit the release of histamine, which is responsible for allergic symptoms and asthma attacks. Onions are especially beneficial to diabetics, since they are as effective in lowering blood sugar as some prescription drugs.

# Falafel (chickpea patties)

## Ingredients to make 8-9 small patties

115 g/4 ounces dried chickpeas which have been covered with four times their volume in boiling water and soaked overnight

1 medium onion, cut into 8 pieces

2 tbsp fresh coriander (cilantro) leaves, finely chopped

2 cloves garlic, roughly chopped

1 tsp coriander seeds

1 tsp cumin seeds

¼ tsp potassium baking powder

Potassium salt

Cayenne pepper

Olive oil for frying

## Instructions

Drain the soaked chickpeas, and, using the S blade, whizz them in a food processor with the onion and garlic until they become a smooth paste which clumps together. Roughly crush the coriander and cumin seeds with a mortar and pestle then dry-roast them in a medium-hot frying pan for about half a minute to release the aromas. Stir the spices, seasonings and baking powder into the chickpea mixture and mix thoroughly.

Preheat a frying pan (skillet) over a medium heat and pour in olive oil to coat the bottom of the pan. Take tablespoons of the chickpea mixture, and, using your hands, form them into little patties measuring about 2 inches in diameter. When the oil is hot, gently lower the patties into it and cook for about 5 minutes on each side. Handle them gently when turning them over - I use a pair of flat tongs such as those used for turning fried fish. Drain the falafels on absorbent kitchen paper and serve hot or cold as a starter, snack, packed lunch or light supper dish with Cacik (page 136) and a green salad, or tucked into a folded round of unleavened bread (page 134) and topped with shredded lettuce and Garlic Crème (page 129).

## What It's Good For

Chickpeas are very rich in protein, and are a good source of many other nutrients, including calcium, magnesium, iron, copper and some of the B vitamins.
Falafels are a Middle Eastern dish and are often served stuffed into pitta bread and topped with salad and yoghurt. Always buy pulses/ legumes (members of the bean and lentil family) with the longest "sell-by" date you can find. Lengthy storage makes them tough.

# Cream of Mushroom Soup

## Ingredients for 2 servings

115 g/4 ounces/1 cup fresh
   mushrooms, roughly chopped

1 medium onion, roughly chopped

1 pint boiling water

2 tbsp extra virgin olive oil

1 rounded tbsp wheat-free miso

1 rounded tbsp brown rice flour

1 tbsp fresh parsley, finely
   chopped

1 tbsp soya (soy) cream

Freshly ground black pepper

## Instructions

Heat the oil in a large saucepan over a medium heat and sweat the onions for a few minutes until translucent. Add the mushrooms, turn up the heat and stir-fry briskly for about 3 minutes. Sprinkle the brown rice flour over the mushrooms and onions, and stir it in thoroughly.

Dissolve the miso in the boiling water and pour over the mushrooms and onions. Stir well, bring back to the boil then turn the heat down to low, cover the pan and simmer for 20 minutes.

Remove the pan from the heat, and whizz the soup in the pan with a hand blender until you achieve the consistency you want. Stir in the soya cream and chopped parsley, season with freshly ground black pepper and serve immediately.

## What It's Good For

The main benefit of common (white) mushrooms is their vitamin and mineral content. They are rich in B vitamins, iron, copper, zinc and chromium. Some varieties of mushroom, especially the shiitake, are now known to have special medicinal properties due to their content of *lentinan*, a substance with anti-cancer properties.

# Spinach and Lentil Soup

## Ingredients for 6 servings

1.2 litres/2 pints/4 cups water

115g/4 ounces/½ cup brown lentils or Puy lentils*

250 g/9 ounces fresh spinach

1 large onion, chopped

2 tbsp miso

1 tbsp tomato purée (paste)

1 tbsp fresh lemon juice

Freshly ground black pepper

*These are small green speckled lentils. They are best for this soup as they retain a slightly chewy texture which contrasts well with the smoothness of the spinach.

## Instructions

Put the water, lentils and chopped onion in a large saucepan and bring to the boil, then cover the pan and simmer gently for 30 minutes.

Meanwhile, wash the spinach in a sinkful of cold water and drain in a colander. Twist off any tough, fibrous stalks from the spinach leaves, then take bundles of leaves, and shred them coarsely with a knife. Turn the shredded spinach bundles round 90 degrees and shred crosswise so that the spinach ends up roughly chopped.

When the lentils are ready, stir in the miso and tomato purée (paste), and incorporate thoroughly, then stir in the spinach. Put the lid on and leave over a low heat for 5 minutes or until the spinach has wilted and softened.

Using a hand blender, briefly whizz the soup while still in the pan, so that most of the lentils are still a little chewy, while the rest of the soup is thick and smooth. Stir in the freshly ground black pepper. If you wish, you could also pour in a little soya cream before serving.

## What It's Good For

Lentils and walnuts are both good sources of an important B vitamin known as folic acid. This is one of the vitamins most likely to be in short supply in a diet consisting mostly of convenience foods because it is easily destroyed by food processing and lengthy storage.

Spinach is also an excellent source of iron, but do remember that iron from plant foods is not very well absorbed unless the meal also contains vitamin C. The lemon juice in this recipe will help you absorb the iron, and you may also want to finish the meal with some fresh fruit.

# Potato Pancakes with a Spinach, Mushroom and Goat's Cheese Filling

## Ingredients to make 1 pancake

2 medium-sized waxy potatoes

55 g/2 ounces/½ cup mushrooms, thinly sliced*

25 g/1 ounce hard goat's cheese, finely grated

50 g spinach, washed and shredded

Olive oil

Freshly ground black pepper

*You could use some of the more unusual varieties of mushrooms such as shiitake if you would like a change.

## Instructions

Preheat a 9½ inch diameter frying pan (skillet) over a medium heat until very hot, then add 2 tbsp oil.

Coarsely grate the potatoes as quickly as you can to prevent browning, then transfer them to the hot frying pan. Using the tip of a spatula, distribute them evenly in the pan and press down to flatten. Cover the frying pan and leave the pancake to cook for one minute then turn the heat down low-medium and leave it to cook for a further 9 minutes.

Remove the pan from the heat and carefully slide the pancake on to a large plate. Cover the pancake with a second plate, then invert the plates, thus turning the pancake over. Replace the frying pan over a medium heat. When hot, add another tbsp oil, then carefully slide the pancake back into the pan to cook the other side and replace the lid. Turn the heat down again after one minute and then cook for a further 5 minutes. Remove from the pan and keep warm.

While the pancake is cooking, stir-fry the mushrooms in 2 tbsp hot olive oil until golden. Stir in the shredded spinach and toss until wilted. Remove from the heat and spoon on to one half of the potato pancake. Cover with grated cheese, season with freshly grated black pepper then fold the other half of the pancake over the filling and serve immediately.

## What It's Good For

Waxy potatoes allow you to make a deliciously succulent pancake without the need for egg. Potatoes are rich in potassium, and also lysine, a protein constituent (amino acid) which is low in most plant foods except beans and lentils, and is especially needed by herpes sufferers.
Goat's cheese is also a good source of protein (including lysine).
Spinach is a wonderful source of iron and other minerals, and mushrooms provide B vitamins and chromium.

# Crab Terrine

## Ingredients for 4-6 servings

1 medium-sized crab, dressed*

115 g/4 ounces silken tofu (see page 26)

2 tbsp sunflower oil

15 g/½ ounce gelatine powder

Soya or sheep's milk yoghurt as required†

1 tbsp fresh lemon juice

3 tbsp water

Potassium salt

Freshly ground black pepper

*You can either buy the crab ready-dressed, or, for a better flavour, dress it yourself just before making this recipe (see next page).

†If using soya yoghurt, choose a thick variety such as Sojasun. Sheep's yoghurt is sharper than soya yoghurt, so use it if you prefer a slightly more acidic flavour.

## Instructions

Put the 3 tbsp water in a small dish, and sprinkle the gelatine powder over it to soften.

Whizz the silken tofu, brown crab meat, sunflower oil, potassium salt and lemon juice until smooth, in a food processor using the S blade. If you are using a firm variety of silken tofu such as Sanchi Organic Tofu, you will also need to add 2 tbsp of water to soften the consistency.

Heat 2 tbsp water in a small saucepan over a moderate heat until it is boiling vigorously, then remove it from the heat, empty out the water and immediately put the softened gelatine into the hot pan. If the pan retains heat well, the gelatine should then dissolve and quickly become runny when stirred. (If it does not, you will need to boil some water in a larger pan and then put the smaller pan inside it so that you can heat the gelatine to the runny stage without scorching it).

Pour some of the whizzed crab mixture into the pan of gelatine and stir thoroughly, then pour this mixture back into the food processor with the rest. Process again briefly until the gelatine has been thoroughly

## What It's Good For

As they grow larger, crabs have to grow a new (soft) shell inside the old one. This soft shell can be scraped out and is not only delicious but extremely nutritious and rich with the bone-nourishing minerals calcium, magnesium and zinc.

Crabs are also an exceptionally good source of selenium, a trace element which is very depleted in British soil. Like all seafood, crabs are a good source of iodine, which can help prevent breast disease in women and is also important for your thyroid gland, which governs your metabolism.

### Dressing a Crab

Ask the fishmonger to prise it open for you if you don't know how to do this, and to remove the inedible "dead men's fingers" (contrary to popular belief, they are not poisonous). Ask for a male crab if you want one with more white meat.

Dressing a crab just means prising the meat out from every little nook and cranny of the crab. It can take up to an hour. Keeping the white meat separate from the brown meat (which is also known as the "cream" of the crab) use strong kitchen scissors to cut through the internal body shell and up the small leg segments before prising them open, and a skewer to ease out the meat. Crack the large claws with a hammer.

incorporated, scraping down the sides with a rubber spatula half-way through.

Then, using the same spatula, scrape the crab mixture into a measuring jug with a capacity of at least one pint (600 ml) and fold in the shredded white crab meat. Season with freshly ground black pepper. If the contents of the jug do not reach the 1 pint mark, top them up with soya or sheep's yoghurt.

Mix well, then pour into a small loaf tin or long plastic mould which has been lined with clingfilm. Chill for several hours before serving.

*Serving suggestions*

* Cut into slabs and serve as a starter on shredded lettuce with wheat-free crispbread or crackers,

* Dollop on to warm Potato Cakes Grand Prix as a delicious topping.

## More About Selenium

Scientists now know that people who eat a selenium-rich diet have a much lower risk of getting a heart attack or cancer. Selenium should be absorbed from the soil into our cereal foods. Unfortunately the soil in most areas of the UK, New Zealand, Finland and parts of China are very poor in selenium. So we have to make up for it by consuming more Brazil nuts, seafood and selenium supplements. Selenium is also needed to turn our thyroid hormone into its active form and to make an antioxidant enzyme, glutathione peroxidase.

# Crudités

## Ingredients for 2 servings

1 large carrot

1 large green (bell) pepper

1 large sweet red (bell) pepper

2 stalks of celery

Half a mooli* radish

Half a cucumber

*Mooli radishes are long, white radishes about twice the size of carrots. They are often used in Oriental cookery, and can be found in larger supermarkets. If you cannot obtain one, use ordinary radishes.

## Instructions

Cut the radish and carrot into 3-inch segments then slice these lengthwise first one way and then the other to make sticks.

Cut around the stalk of the peppers and remove it, then cut the peppers into eight pieces lengthwise. Discard the seeds but retain as much of the white pith as possible.

Using a sharp knife or vegetable peeler, peel the outside of the celery stalks so that the tough fibres are stripped away, then cut the stalks in half.

Cut the cucumber into 3-inch segments then cut each segment into four pieces lengthwise.

Arrange the crudités on a plate, with a selection of dips for people to help themselves.

Suitable dips from this book are those on pages 47 and also:

- Sour cream (page 128)
- Hummus (page 41)
- Garlic crème (page 129).

## What It's Good For

Delicious crunchy raw vegetables are an ideal party snack. Among other this, this dish provides Carrots: beta carotene, Peppers: vitamin C and flavonoids, Celery: organic sodium (unlike sodium from salt, this is not harmful) and coumarins, which help to release fluid retention, Cucumber: silica (good for bone and skin strength), Mooli radish: sulphur compounds, which are highly beneficial for the liver.

# Potato Ravioli

## Ingredients for about 24 small ravioli (2 servings)

One quantity of Potato Gnocci dough (see page 105)

2 tbsp pesto sauce (page 101)

25 g/1 ounce finely grated goat's cheese* for filling plus 55 g/2 ounces for topping

*Choose a hard variety that grates easily

## Instructions

Divide the potato dough in half and form each half into a ball. Using a rolling pin, roll out the dough ball into a sheet about ¼ inch thick.

Using a glass tumbler or pastry cutter with a diameter of about 2½ inches, cut out as many rounds from this sheet as you can.

Bring a large saucepan of water to the boil.

Dot the centre of each round with a small blob of pesto sauce and a pinch of grated cheese, then fold the rounds over and, using the very tips of your fingers, carefully pinch the edges together to form a tiny "pasty".

You should not have trouble getting the edges to stay together if your pinches are tiny enough, but if you do you could dampen the edges of the rounds with a little water before pressing together.

As you prepare the ravioli, put them on a plate then gently slide them off the plate into the gently boiling water. Cook for 60-80 seconds then remove them from the water with a slotted spoon. Serve immediately, sprinkled with the rest of the grated cheese.

## What It's Good For

Based on my nutritional consulting work, I would say that about half of all people with a food intolerance have problems with cow's milk products. As with other food intolerances, these problems can be anything from headaches to eczema, joint pains or irritable bowel syndrome. Substituting goat or sheep's milk, cheese and yoghurt is not the answer for everyone (and you should certainly not eat them every day, for fear of developing an intolerance to these products too) but go ahead and enjoy an occasional recipe like this if it does not cause you any symptoms.

# Lamb's Liver Terrine with Onions and Thyme

## Ingredients for 4-6 servings

300 g/10 ounces organic lamb's liver, roughly cut into chunks

150 g/5 ounces onions, finely chopped

2 walnut-sized knobs of coconut oil

1 tsp dried thyme

Potassium salt

Freshly-ground black pepper

## Instructions

Heat one knob of coconut oil in a frying pan (skillet) over a medium heat, add the onions, and sweat them for 5 minutes until translucent.

Keeping the pan hot, remove the onions from the pan with a slotted spoon into the bowl of a food processor fitted with the S blade, then add the second knob of coconut oil followed by the chunks of lamb's liver. Stir and fry for about 5 minutes, until cooked, then add the liver to the onions in the food processor. Season with potassium salt.

Scraping down the sides with a rubber spatula from time to time, whizz the liver and onions until the mixture is finely ground and clumps together.

While still warm, empty the mixture into a terrine dish with a capacity of about half a litre/¾ pint and smooth down the surface with a fork. Allow to cool and when cold cover the dish with a piece of absorbent kitchen paper (to prevent condensation dripping on the contents) followed by a lid or a sheet of clingfilm, and place in the fridge for at least 3 hours. Serve slices of the terrine on wheat– and yeast-free crackers, crispbread or pumpernickel, or on a bed of lettuce with salad and mayonnaise.

## What It's Good For

Warnings about liver containing poisonous amounts of vitamin A are only true when it comes from intensively-reared animals— their feed contains artificially large amounts of vitamin A added as a growth-promoter. The vitamin collects in their liver, which can then contain up to 20 times the normal amount of vitamin A. Organic liver does not have this problem. Liver provides protein, vitamin A, B vitamins and many minerals including chromium and zinc. It is well worth consuming liver occasionally since I believe that vitamin A deficiency is more common than we realize. Not all of us are efficient at making this vitamin from beta carotene.

# Main Meals

Lots of people are confused about how much they should eat at different meals. The truth is, a heavy meal eaten late in the day is much more easily turned into body fat. This is because you would normally be sleeping at night and cannot use it up like your other meals. The old maxim "Breakfast like a King, lunch like a prince and dine like a pauper" is absolutely true!

# Organic Chicken Sauté with Vegetables and Garlic

## Ingredients for 2 servings

2 medium portions organic chicken

1 x 400 g/14 ounce can chopped plum tomatoes

4 medium potatoes, peeled and cut in half

1 large onion, roughly diced

1 large carrot, cut into 1-inch segments

115 g/4 ounces/1 cup white mushrooms, thickly sliced

4 cloves garlic, peeled and roughly chopped

2 tbsp extra virgin olive oil

2 tbsp rice flour

1 tbsp soya cream

Potassium salt

Black pepper

## Instructions

This is a one-pot meal made in a pressure cooker. Season the chicken portions with potassium salt then coat thoroughly with rice flour. Heat the olive oil in the pressure cooker with the lid off then add the chicken pieces. Fry over a high heat until golden and crisp on both sides (this seals in the juices), then stir in the onion and garlic, and continue stirring until they begin to soften. Pour in the chopped tomatoes, stir, put the lid on and bring the pressure cooker up to full steam. Maintaining a steady pressure, cook for 20 minutes.

Put the pressure cooker in a sink of cold water to bring the pressure down and enable you to remove the lid. Stir the contents, then add the remaining vegetables to the pan, fitting them neatly around the chicken and ensuring they are all coated with the sauce. (If necessary add a little water to the pan to enable this). Replace the lid and heat again to full steam. Once again maintaining a steady pressure, cook for a further 12 minutes.

Put the pressure cooker in cold water again and once it is safe to do so, remove the lid, check that the vegetables are tender, and remove the chicken and vegetable pieces to a heated serving dish with the aid of a slotted spoon. Keep warm. Replace the pressure cooker on the stove, without

## What It's Good For

Even free-range chickens may be fed standard commercial feed which contains antibiotics, dung from other chickens, and other unsavoury items. We do not know what kind of residues remain in the bird's meat and fat, and how they can affect our health. Eating organic chicken overcomes all these potential problems. Besides, the flavour is far better.

Chicken is an excellent, low-fat source of protein - even with its skin left on. Protein is essential for all our body processes, including the important work of our liver in removing toxins from our blood.

**Special Equipment**

A pressure cooker

putting the lid on, and turn up the heat until you can fast-boil the sauce remaining in the pan. Keep stirring and reduce to about 2-3 ladlefuls of thick sauce. Remove from the heat and add 1 tbsp soya cream, plus some freshly ground black pepper. Stir through and pour the sauce over the chicken and vegetables. Serve immediately.

# Baked Potatoes with Salmon and Sour Cream

**Ingredients for 2 servings**

2 baking potatoes, well scrubbed

115 g/4 ounces fresh salmon, filleted

1 spring onion (scallion), finely sliced

Soya milk

1 tsp fresh dill, chopped

Potassium salt

Freshly ground black pepper

**Instructions**

Preheat the oven to 200°C/400°F/Gas mark 6.

Prick the potatoes all over with a fork, and bake them for 45 minutes or until they feel soft when you squeeze them. Poach the salmon in a few tablespoons of water in a lidded pan over a low heat for five minutes, until the fish flakes easily.

Remove the potatoes from the oven and slice in half lengthways. Scoop out the potato flesh, leaving the skins intact. Mash the potato flesh with a little soya milk and seasoning, then gently fold in the spring onion and salmon flakes, trying not to break them up too much, and pile the mixture into the potato skin halves. Return to the oven for 15 minutes to heat through, then serve with a generous topping of sour cream (see page 128) and a sprinkling of dill.

**What It's Good For**

Like herrings (see recipe on page 31), salmon is a so-called "oily" fish, rich in omega 3 oils which help prevent red blood cells from clumping together and causing heart attacks. You may not know that these oily fish themselves are a far richer source of omega 3 oils than fish oil supplements. Salmon is also an excellent source of protein, needed by your liver to process toxins.

# Red Thai Curry with Pan-Fried Tofu

## Ingredients for 1 serving

3 thick slices from a block of firm tofu

1 cm/½ inch piece cut from a block of creamed coconut

½ cup mixed frozen vegetables (e.g. carrots and red sweet [bell] peppers diced small, peas, sweetcorn [corn])

1 portion uncooked vermicelli rice noodles or 1 portion cooked brown rice

150 ml/¼ pint/½ cup water

2 tbsp groundnut oil for frying

1 tbsp brown rice flour

2 tsp red Thai curry paste (more if you like it stronger)

Potassium salt

Cayenne pepper

## Instructions

Cut the tofu into bite-size pieces, pat dry with kitchen paper, sprinkle with potassium salt and cayenne pepper and coat well with brown rice flour. Heat the oil in a frying pan (skillet). When hot enough for the tofu to sizzle, carefully put the pieces in the pan and fry on each side for 1-2 minutes or until golden. Drain on absorbent kitchen paper.

Heat the water in a saucepan. Add the curry paste and coconut cream, stirring until dissolved. Add the frozen vegetables, put the lid on the saucepan and simmer for a few minutes.

Place the vermicelli rice noodles in a bowl. Boil a kettleful of water and pour the water generously over the noodles, leaving them plenty of room to swell. Leave for 2 minutes then run some cold water into the bowl before draining the noodles thoroughly in a large sieve. If using rice, heat the rice in a tightly lidded pan over a medium heat with 2 tablespoons of water.

When the vegetables are heated through, stir in the fried tofu pieces and coat with the sauce. Serve the rice or noodles with the vegetables and tofu on top and a little of the sauce spooned over.

## What It's Good For

Tofu, with its richness of hormone-balancing compounds, and coconut cream, with the anti-viral properties of the coconut oil it contains, are key ingredients here, with mixed vegetables providing a rich balance of antioxidant nutrients, and cayenne pepper (found in the curry paste) helping to warm the circulation and improve the digestion. This is a delicious meal which can be put together in only 10 minutes.

# Stuffed Sweet Peppers with Wild Rice and Porcini Mushrooms

## Ingredients for 2 servings

2 medium to large sweet (bell) peppers

125 g/4½ ounces/½ cup firm tofu

4 tbsp cooked brown rice, to include 1 tsp cooked wild or red rice

1 small to medium onion, finely chopped

1 small handful dried porcini mushrooms which have been soaked in boiling water for half an hour and then finely chopped

4 cloves garlic, finely chopped

2 tbsp soya (soy) milk

2 tbsp extra virgin olive oil

1 tsp fresh basil, finely chopped

Potassium salt

Freshly ground black pepper

## Instructions

Preheat the oven to 180°C/350°F/gas mark 4. Blanch the peppers for two minutes in a pan of boiling water then remove and drain. Sweat the chopped onion slowly in the olive oil over a low heat, with the lid on the pan. Cut the tops (with stalks) off the peppers and save them to make lids. Remove the seeds with a teaspoon.

In a blender or food processor (with S blade), whizz the tofu and soya milk, scraping the sides down with a spatula from time to time, until smooth and creamy.

When the onions are soft, add the garlic, chopped mushrooms, cooked rice, basil and seasoning. Stir-fry together in the pan for half a minute, then fold in the creamed tofu. Remove from the heat, and keep folding with a spoon to ensure that all the ingredients are thoroughly incorporated.

Stuff the peppers with this mixture and press it in firmly. Replace the tops of the peppers. Stand the peppers up in an oiled oven-proof dish (or lay them down if they won't stand), brush with olive oil, and bake for 45 minutes or until tender.

Using a sharp knife, cut each pepper across into 4-6 slices and serve with Potato Cakes Grand Prix (page 98) or Garlic Potatoes Corfu Style (see page 92).

## What It's Good For

The main ingredients of this dish are tofu and sweet peppers. See page 28 for the benefits of tofu and other soya products. Sweet (i.e. capsicum or bell) peppers are an excellent source of vitamin C and flavonoids. Many of the flavonoids are concentrated in the white pith, so try not to throw it away. Green sweet peppers are simply an unripe version of red ones, and contain less carotene.

# Mexican Tortillas with Garlic, Lime and Refried Beans

## To make 4 lazy tortillas

<u>90 g/3 ounces/3 heaped tbsp finely ground yellow polenta meal</u>

<u>20 g/1 ounce/1 heaped tbsp buckwheat flour</u>

<u>200 ml/generous 6 fluid oz/¾ cup water</u>

## Instructions

When cooked, these tortillas look just like the real thing—on one side only. On the other side they look like pancakes! Needless to say, hide the pancake side with your filling and no-one will notice the difference.

Mix the ingredients thoroughly. Depending on your flours, you may need a little more or a little less water, so don't be afraid to experiment a bit. Heat a dry non-stick frying pan (skillet) over a medium to high heat. Stir the mixture then pour in a ladleful and gently shake the pan so that it quickly spreads out on all sides to the thickness of a pancake. Try to keep the shape circular, and aim to make the tortillas about 6 inches in diameter.

After about one minute, when the top has set and the edges start to curl upwards, flip the tortilla over and cook the other side. Press down with a spatula and cook for another minute or until the bottom is looking slightly floury with brown specks.

Make the other three tortillas in the same way, and stack them, separated by a layer of absorbent kitchen paper, until you are ready to fill them.

## What It's Good For

It would be very difficult to pack any more nutrients into a meal than you can get from this lovely dish. Here are just a few examples of what it provides.
Beans and polenta flour: high-class protein combination.
Tomatoes: anti-cancer carotene lycopene.
Raw garlic: blood sterilizing, anti-candida and anti-cancer action.
Onion: anti-allergy and anti-cancer flavonoid quercetin.
Lime: vitamin C and blood vessel strengthening flavonoids.

## To make the filling

450 g/1 lb/2 cups cooked pinto
    beans (see page 19), mashed
    roughly with a potato masher or
    fork

4 fresh tomatoes, skinned and
    chopped

1 large onion, chopped

The flesh of 1 small lime, cut in
    four and sliced

Plus 1 tsp grated lime zest

2 green hot chilli peppers, cut into
    long, thin strips

4 cloves garlic, crushed

2 tbsp fresh coriander leaf
    (cilantro) chopped

2 tbsp extra virgin olive oil

1 tsp black mustard seeds

Tamari sauce

Potassium salt

Shredded iceberg lettuce and Garlic
    Crème (page 129) to garnish

## Instructions

Heat the olive oil over a medium heat in a deep frying pan (skillet), or preferably a stir-fry pan, and add the mustard seeds. When they begin to pop, add the chopped onion, 3½ cloves of the crushed garlic, and the chilli pepper strips.

Stir-fry until they are beginning to soften, then add the lime flesh and zest and fry for another two minutes, gently turning occasionally with a spoon without breaking up the lime pieces.

Fold in the chopped tomatoes and allow to cook for a further 2 minutes, occasionally turning the mixture, until the tomatoes are soft. Add the mashed beans, chopped coriander, the rest of the chopped garlic, a few dashes of tamari sauce and some potassium salt, fold in gently, turn down the heat to low and cover the pan. Leave for 5 minutes to heat through, occasionally turning the ingredients gently with a spoon. The beans will soften and blend with the other ingredients.

Meanwhile heat up the tortillas under the grill (broiler) and keep warm. When the filling is ready, hold a tortilla "pancake side up" in your hand and pile filling into it, squeezing the sides slightly together. Cover the top of the exposed filling with a handful of shredded iceberg lettuce and pour over a few spoonfuls of Garlic Crème.

## Variation

You can also make enchiladas by rolling the refried bean filling up in the corn pancakes described on page 28, laying the rolls seam-side down, and topping with a tomato, garlic and chilli sauce and a dollop of Garlic Crème.

Make a tomato salsa to go with either of these dishes, using finely chopped tomatoes, diced avocado pear, chilli pepper, coriander leaf (cilantro) and capers plus a squeeze of lemon juice and a dash of Tabasco chilli sauce.

# Rejuvenation Soup (a one-pot meal)

## Ingredients for 6 servings

1 organic chicken or duck carcass

The giblets (liver, neck and heart only)

1.7 litres/3 pints/6 cups water

Approx 200 g/7 ounces rice vermicelli

4 dark green cabbage leaves, shredded

2 carrots, sliced

2 tomatoes, roughly chopped

1 large onion, chopped

2 tbsp brown miso

Black pepper

## Special Equipment

A pressure cooker

## Instructions

You would normally use the remains of a roast chicken or duck for this soup, but any small bones will do, for instance those left after filleting a chicken.

Cut any greeny-yellow marks off the liver (these are bitter and come from bile). Put the bones in a pressure cooker with the giblets and water and press down on the carcass to ensure it is covered with water. Bring to full steam and cook for 45 minutes. Cool the pressure cooker in a sink of cold water until you can open the lid, then strain the stock through a sieve into a large saucepan. Dissolve the miso in the stock, season with black pepper and add the vegetables.

Once the contents of the sieve have cooled, use your hands to pick the remains of any meat off the neck and bones, and put them in the saucepan. Crumble the liver and thinly slice the heart, and put these in the pan too. Discard the remains of the carcass.

Now bring the pan to the boil and simmer for 30 minutes. Add the rice vermicelli and leave to soak in the soup for 2 minutes before stirring and serving. This soup makes a complete meal and can be refrigerated once cool and reheated as needed.

## What It's Good For

Here is a great way to use the giblets from a chicken or duck as well as the bones which normally get thrown away. In effect, you are getting a couple more meals out of the bird.
Liver is rich in vitamin A, folic acid, iron, copper, zinc and B vitamins.
Bones are rich in calcium, magnesium and many other minerals, as well as glycine, which helps your liver to process toxins.
With antioxidants in the dark green cabbage leaves, and all the vitamins in the miso, eating this soup regularly could seriously rejuvenate you!

# Plaice Meunière with Mustard, Lemon and Parsley Sauce

## Ingredients for 2 servings

2 large plaice fillets

3 tbsp extra virgin olive oil plus 2 tbsp for frying

Juice of half a lemon

1 dessertspoon fresh or 1 tsp dried parsley, chopped

Brown rice flour

½ tsp arrowroot powder

½ tsp yellow mustard powder

Potassium salt

Black pepper

## Instructions

Combine the 3 tbsp oil in a small saucepan with the lemon juice and heat very gently. Blend the arrowroot and mustard powders with a tablespoon of water and stir into the mixture in the saucepan. Stir until it thickens, then remove from the heat and season with potassium salt and black pepper. Stir in the parsley.

Heat 2 tbsp oil in a frying pan. Season the plaice fillets and coat thoroughly with rice flour. When the oil is hot, put the fillet in the pan, skin side up. Cook for 2 minutes or until the bottom is beginning to crisp and turn golden. Turn over and cook the other side for 1-2 minutes, pressing down a little with a spatula as the fish will curl up slightly. Drain the fish on absorbent kitchen paper and keep warm. Repeat with the other fillet if it did not fit in the same pan.

When ready to serve, whisk the sauce, and pour over the fish. A good vegetable accompaniment would be Diced New Potatoes and Courgettes with Pesto Coating (see page 101).

*Variation*

This sauce can also be served with poached halibut.

(see page 101)

## What It's Good For

Fish is not just an excellent source of good quality protein, but is easy to digest and contains little or no saturated fat. This makes it ideal for someone whose liver is under stress.

Olive oil contains fatty acids which help to combat the yeast *Candida albicans*. Extra virgin olive oil is also now known to help preserve our mental powers as we age.

Many people who find it hard to digest fats seem to have much less of a problem with olive oil.

# Hot Spicy Prawns with Rice Noodles and Mixed Vegetables

## Ingredients for 1 serving

115 g/4 ounces rice noodles

115 g/4 ounces/½ cup frozen
   mixed vegetables diced small
   (e.g. peas, carrots, peppers,
   [sweet]corn)

1 handful frozen peeled prawns*

1 tsp tamari sauce* or Thai fish
   sauce*

4 tbsp extra virgin olive oil

Potassium salt

Cayenne pepper

*Caution: These contain salt

## Special Equipment

A stir-fry pan

## Instructions

Put the frozen prawns and vegetables in a small lidded saucepan with 2 tbsp olive oil and heat gently until thawed. Continue cooking gently for 5 minutes with the lid off to allow the juices to evaporate. Remove from the heat, sprinkle with cayenne pepper and stir.

Follow the instructions on the rice noodles packet with regard to soaking them in hot water, although you may find that halving the soaking time indicated on the packet produces a better result (ideally they should still be definitely "al dente" because stir-frying will finish cooking them). I like to use thin noodles—slightly thicker than vermicelli—which take only 2 minutes to soak.

As soon as the noodles have finished soaking, drain them quickly in a large sieve and put them in a bowl. Pour cold water over them, strain them again (throw the water away) and suspend them over the empty bowl to catch any drips.

Heat a stir-fry pan over a medium heat. When hot, add 2 tbsp olive oil and then the rice noodles. Stir-fry for about 20 seconds, then add potassium salt and tamari sauce or fish sauce and stir-fry for another 20 seconds. By now the noo-

This is delicious and satisfying dish for the kind of person who often arrives home late, tired and hungry, and would rather order a take-away or pizza than start cooking. Now you will never need another take-away. Making this dish takes less time than waiting for your take-away, and costs a fraction of the amount. When cooked in this way, frozen vegetables are rich in vitamins and minerals. The vegetables are frozen soon after harvest and do not then lose nutrients like those which hang around in shops and then at home for several days. But if you defrost frozen

dles should be soft. Add the prawns and vegetables and stir-fry together briefly until thoroughly incorporated. Pile on to a plate and eat immediately.

## Variations

Instead of prawns I often use fish fillets (salmon, whiting, haddock etc) which can be poached in a few tablespoons of water in a lidded pan over a low heat for five minutes, then flaked and added to the cooked vegetables. My favourite variation is to use finely shredded green cabbage instead of frozen vegetables. Use a mandolin-type appliance to shred it, then briefly stir-fry it in olive oil in the stir-fry pan, add 2 tbsp water, cover the stir-fry pan tightly, and leave it over a low to medium heat to steam for 5 minutes. Stir the cabbage into the noodles as you did with the frozen vegetables.

You could also use small pieces of leftover steamed vegetables such as broccoli and carrots. Just add them to the noodles then put a lid over the stir-fry pan and leave to heat through for 2 minutes over the lowest possible heat before serving.

**vegetables and then throw away their defrost liquid, you will be throwing away most of their vitamins. Likewise if you boil them and then throw away the cooking water.
Like other seafood, prawns are rich in nutrients from the sea, including zinc and iodine.**

# Baked Salmon Parcels with Lime and Dill

### Ingredients for each serving

One salmon fillet weighing about
115 g/4 ounces

Limes (one for each 3-4 fillets),
thinly sliced

Olive oil

Fresh dill weed, roughly chopped

Potassium salt

Freshly ground black pepper

### Instructions

Preheat the oven to gas mark 4

Brush the salmon fillets with olive oil then season with potassium salt and freshly ground black pepper. Sprinkle a pinch of chopped dill over the fish, then lay 3 overlapping slices of lime on top. Place each fillet carefully in the centre of a piece of baking foil, and fold the foil around the fish, tucking in the edges to make a parcel. If you wish to avoid aluminium, it is possible to make the parcels with baking parchment or grease-proof paper instead. Use a stapler to hold the edges of the parcel together. Lay the parcels in an open oven-proof dish or tray and bake in the oven for 25 minutes or until the fish is opaque throughout. Never over-cook fish - it is at its best when only just done.

Serve immediately, with Sour Cream (page 128) and mixed vegetables, or with a Baked Rice dish (pages 88 and 89).

### What It's Good For

Like herrings (see recipe on page 31), salmon is a so-called "oily" fish, rich in omega 3 oils which help prevent red blood cells from clumping together and causing heart attacks.
You may not know that these oily fish themselves are a far richer source of omega 3 oils than fish oil supplements.
Salmon is also an excellent source of protein, needed by your liver to process toxins.

# Pasta Spirals Baked with a Sauce of Tomatoes, Mushrooms and Olives and Topped with Sour Cream

## Ingredients for 4 servings

700 g/1½ lb/3 cups fresh tomatoes, skinned and chopped (you could also use good quality plum tomatoes canned in natural juice)

225 g/8 ounces/1 cup onions, finely chopped

225 g/8 ounces/4 handfuls pasta spirals made from rice or corn

225 g/8 ounces/1 cup mushrooms, finely diced

2 tbsp tomato purée (paste)

6 black olives, stoned and cut in four

(not ones preserved in lemon or vinegar)

4 cloves garlic, peeled and chopped

Extra virgin olive oil

1 tbsp fresh basil, chopped

1 tbsp fresh chives, chopped

Potassium salt

Freshly ground black pepper

## Instructions

Preheat the oven to 180°C/350°F/gas mark 4. In a large saucepan, gently fry the chopped onion in 4 tbsp olive oil until soft but not brown. Stir in the chopped garlic and cook for half a minute, then stir in the chopped tomatoes. Put a lid on the pan and cook over a medium heat for 15 minutes to break down the tomatoes. Fry the diced mushrooms in 3 tbsp olive oil until golden.

Remove the lid from the saucepan, add the tomato purée, mushrooms, olive pieces and potassium salt, and continue to boil for 45 minutes over a medium heat without the lid until the sauce is reduced to a thick consistency. Stir in the chopped basil.

Put the pasta spirals in a large pan of fast boiling water and cook according to the directions on the packet until they are just "al dente". Do not overcook them. Run some cold water into the pan as soon as they are ready, drain them, put them in an oven-proof dish, and thoroughly mix them with 2 tbsp olive oil. Add the pasta sauce and stir together.

Cover the dish and bake in the oven for 45 minutes. Serve with sour cream (see page 128) spooned on top and a sprinkling of chives.

## What It's Good For

There are lots of goodies in this recipes, including chromium and B vitamins from the mushrooms, anti-cancer lycopene from the tomatoes, soya in the Sour Cream, and methionine in the pasta spirals (if made from rice). Methionine is turned to glutathione in your liver, and used to help it detoxify pollutants. Extra virgin olive oil is useful in the treatment of candidiasis, and is now known to help you retain your brainpower in older age.

# Brown Beans in a Spicy Tomato Sauce with Creamed Potatoes

## Ingredients for 4 servings

450 g/1 lb/2 cups cooked borlotti beans* (see page 19)

450 g/1 lb/2½ cups tomatoes, skinned and roughly chopped

4 cloves garlic, peeled and crushed

2 tbsp extra virgin olive oil

2 tbsp tomato purée (paste)

1 tbsp wheat-free miso

1 tsp porcini mushroom powder

Dried or fresh chopped herbs according to taste: thyme, parsley, tarragon, basil

Cayenne pepper

*Borlotti beans are mainly used in Italian cooking. They look a little like kidney beans but are fatter, with a rich brown colour. If you cannot find them, use red kidney beans.

## Instructions

Heat the olive oil in a large saucepan over a medium heat, then add the tomatoes. Crush them with the back of a kitchen spoon until they begin to release their juice, then dissolve the miso in the juice. Add herbs, seasonings, cooked beans and porcini mushroom powder, stir to incorporate thoroughly, then put the lid on the pan and simmer gently for 1 hour, stirring occasionally.

At the end of this time, remove the lid. Break some of the beans up by roughly mashing them with a fork or potato masher. The beans should end up just covered by sauce, so if necessary turn up the heat to fast boil away any excess liquid.

Serve with Creamed Potatoes (next page) and a topping of Sour Cream (see page 128) or Garlic Crème (see page 129).

## What It's Good For

This is another rich and satisfying dish, especially on a winter's evening. Beans are rich in protein, especially the anti-herpes amino acid lysine. Miso is rich in B vitamins. Tomatoes, especially when cooked and concentrated, are loaded with the anti-cancer carotene known as lycopene.

If you have any difficulty with digesting beans, try having them with the Digestive Tea on page 140.

## To make the Creamed Potatoes

Allow one large floury potato for each serving

Cold-pressed sunflower oil

(or soya (soy) cream)

Potassium salt

Freshly ground black pepper

## Special Equipment

A potato press

It is difficult to make really good creamed potatoes without a potato press—a metal press shaped like a very large garlic press. Cooked potato chunks are pressed through it, and emerge mashed through small holes, which eliminates all lumps.

N.B. Do not try to make creamed potatoes in a food processor - they will not have a good texture.

Cut the potatoes into chunks and boil them in one inch of water until tender. Remove from the heat. Put the potato press and a large bowl under the hot water tap to warm them so that they will not cool the potatoes too much. Using a slotted spoon, remove a spoonful of potato pieces at a time and put them through the press into the bowl. Using a wooden spoon, stir a few tablespoons of sunflower oil and potato cooking water into the potatoes. Add the seasoning. Keep stirring in the hot water until you have the consistency you want.

Alternatively you could omit the oil, and add soya cream instead. Serve immediately.

## What It's Good For

Potatoes are often thought of as a "fattening" food, but in fact are not at all high in calories. A medium-sized potato provides only about 110 Calories. It is the butter and sauces potatoes are served with, and the oil they are fried in which can make them fattening. Potatoes are rich in potassium and also contain some protein and a little vitamin C.

# German Erbsensuppe (pea soup) with Carrots and Miso
## A one-pot meal

## Ingredients for 4 servings

225 g/8 ounces/1 cup dried
marrowfat peas

115 g/4 ounces/firm, low-fat
sausage (optional) such as
cabanos, cut into large chunks

2 medium potatoes, diced

3 medium carrots, cut into chunks

1 large onion or 1 leek, cut into
chunks

1 tbsp pale miso*

Potassium salt

Freshly ground black pepper

*See page 24

## Special Equipment

A pressure cooker

## Instructions

Pour boiling water over the peas, allowing plenty of room for them to swell, and soak them overnight.

Discard the soaking water, then put the peas in a pressure cooker and cover with cold water. Bring up to full steam then cook for 5 minutes*. Plunge the pressure cooker into a sink of cold water to prevent further cooking and reduce the pressure enough to allow you to open the lid. The peas should be well-softened, and some of them quite mushy.

Stir in the miso then the vegetable and sausage pieces (if used). Pour in just enough water to cover the ingredients, stir well, then bring back to the boil and simmer over a low heat for one hour, stirring occasionally. Season with potassium salt and freshly ground black pepper and serve in large shallow stew plates.

### Variations

In Germany all types of vegetables are thrown into this soup and it is very good for using up leftovers. You can also cook it with yellow split peas instead of marrowfat peas, or, instead of sausage, add some lean chunks of cooked ham to heat through just before serving.

*Older peas may need longer cooking times

## What It's Good For

Like beans, marrowfat peas are very rich in protein, and this dish makes a substantial and highly nutritious complete meal. Sausages are mentioned as an optional ingredient because it is traditional to cook this dish with them. Some types are not particularly fatty and a little goes a long way. But do remember that sausages and ham contain preservatives and often quite a lot of salt.

# Curried White Beans with Aubergine and Tomato

## Ingredients for 2-3 servings

3 handfuls cooked white haricot (navy) beans (see page 19)

1 small aubergine (eggplant), diced

1 medium potato, diced

2 large tomatoes, chopped

1 medium onion, chopped

2 cloves garlic, chopped

½ tsp chilli paste or 2 tsp red Thai curry paste

2 tbsp groundnut oil

1 tsp fresh ginger, chopped

Potassium salt

## Instructions

Using a stir-fry pan, fry the onion in the oil until it turns translucent, then stir in the chopped garlic and ginger, the curry paste and then the beans and stir-fry for half a minute.

Add the diced potatoes and aubergines and stir everything well together.

Stir in the chopped tomatoes and potassium salt. Add water to almost cover the ingredients in the pan.

Cover tightly and leave to simmer over a low heat for 20 minutes. Then turn up the heat to moderate and continue cooking with the lid off, stirring regularly to prevent the ingredients from sticking to the bottom of the pan, for another 20-25 minutes or until the sauce is well reduced and just coats the beans and potatoes.

Serve garnished with fresh coriander (cilantro), accompanied by brown rice or a piece of warm unleavened bread.

see page 19

## What It's Good For

Beans are a good source of B vitamins and protein, especially the amino acid lysine, which is lacking in most other plant foods. Aubergines provide flavonoids and many vitamins and minerals. They are deliciously creamy although they contain no fat or oil. Tomatoes, especially when cooked, are a good source of the anti-cancer carotene known as lycopene. Chilli peppers contain ingredients which help to relieve intestinal flatulence.

# Pancake Pizza

## Ingredients for 2 medium-sized pizzas

*For the batter (dough)*

55 g/2 ounces/1 tbsp fine oatmeal

55 g/2 ounces/1 tbsp spelt flour*

55 g/2 ounces/1½ tbsp soya (soy) flour

250 ml/9 fluid oz/1 cup water

1 rounded tsp potassium baking powder

*See page 26

*For the topping*

Extra virgin olive oil

1 x 400 g can of chopped Italian plum tomatoes

110 g/4 ounces/1 cup grated hard goat or sheep's cheese

## Instructions

Preheat the oven to gas mark 8. Also preheat a lightly oiled frying pan (skillet) over a medium-high heat. Put the tomatoes in a sieve over a bowl to drain off the liquid.

Mix the batter ingredients and beat until smooth. The batter has the right consistency if it settles into a round of about ¼ inch in thickness when poured into the pan.

When the pan is hot, pour in half the batter and tilt a little if necessary to get a round shape. Cook for 1-2 minutes, or until the top of the pancake has set and the bottom is beginning to brown. Turn it over and cook the other side.

Put the cooked pancakes on an oiled baking sheet. Brush them liberally with olive oil, then spread with the chopped tomato flesh (and other topping ingredients if you wish). Cover well with the grated cheese then put on the top shelf of the oven to cook for 10-15 minutes, or until golden and bubbling. Serve immediately.

*Variation*

Add some finely grated carrot and grated goat or sheep's cheese to the pizza base batter, make the pancake then cut it into wedges and eat plain as a snack or accompaniment to a meal, or add toppings and bake as above.

## What It's Good For

This recipe is particularly useful for allergic children, since it is quite similar to real pizza, especially if you can find a really nice goat or sheep's cheese that grates well and melts nicely.

The oatmeal in this recipe provides magnesium, and the tomatoes provide the anti-cancer carotene known as lycopene.

Protein is provided by the combination of the three types of flour and the cheese.

# New England Real Baked Beans

## Ingredients for 4 servings

450 g/1 lb/2 cups cooked pinto*
beans (see page 19)

4 tbsp tomato purée (paste)

4 tbsp blackstrap molasses

600 ml/1 pint/2 cups water which
has been saved after steaming
vegetables

4 bay leaves

Potassium salt

A pinch of cayenne pepper

*You could use white haricot (navy) beans if
you prefer.

## Instructions

Preheat the oven to 140°C/275°F/gas mark 1.

Place the ingredients in a saucepan and bring to the boil, stirring well to dissolve the molasses. Transfer to a casserole dish and cover it tightly.

Place in the oven and cook for 4 hours. It will not spoil if left a couple of hours longer, though you should check occasionally to ensure that the beans are still covered with liquid.

Before serving, transfer the beans to a warm dish and fast-boil the sauce in a saucepan for a few minutes to concentrate it until it reaches your preferred consistency.

Serve the beans with Southern Sweet Potato Bread (see page 86) or with creamed potatoes (page 77).

## What It's Good For

Beans are an excellent source of protein, especially when combined with grains (e.g. cornmeal, rice, oats, rye). They are also rich in B vitamins. Blackstrap molasses is a thick residue left from sugar processing, and contains all the minerals of the sugar cane or sugar beet that were left behind when white or brown sugar was produced: calcium, magnesium, iron, zinc and manganese to name just a few.

# Fillets of Red Mullet Fried Cajun-Style

## Ingredients for 2 servings

4 red mullet fillets*

2 tsp paprika (not the hot variety)

2 tsp onion powder

2 tsp garlic powder

2 tsp dried thyme or oregano

1 tsp cayenne pepper

1 tsp ground black pepper

1 tsp potassium salt

Groundnut oil for frying

*If your fishmonger does not sell them ready-filleted, ask him to fillet them for you.

## Instructions

Using a mortar and pestle, grind the thyme or oregano to a powder, then mix thoroughly with the other dry ingredients. Spread the resulting powder out on a plate.

Dry the fish fillets with absorbent kitchen paper, then press both sides of them firmly into the powder until they are thickly coated.

Heat 4 tbsp groundnut oil in a frying pan (skillet) over a high heat. When the oil is very hot, add the fish fillets, flesh side down, and cook for one minute. Turn over and cook the other side for half a minute, pressing down if necessary to prevent the fillets from curling up.

Drain briefly on absorbent kitchen paper then serve immediately with a vegetable or salad accompaniment. This dish goes very well with German Potato Salad (see page 100).

## What It's Good For

Cajun cookery is hot and spicy and comes from New Orleans and other parts of the Southern United States. Cayenne pepper has two special benefits: it is warming and great for the circulation, and it also has a soothing effect on the digestive system, with the ability to combat intestinal flatulence. Thyme and oregano contain antibacterial and antifungal ingredients and so are useful as part of an anti-candida diet.

# Queen Scallops with Rice Noodles and Spring Greens

## Ingredients for 2 servings

225 g/8 ounces of queen scallops[1]
(excluding shells)

200 g/7 ounces spring greens
(collards)

200 g/7 ounces thin rice noodles[2]

¼ pint/150 ml/½ cup cold water

Olive oil

2 tbsp soya (soy) cream

1 tsp fresh parsley, chopped

1 rounded tsp pale miso dissolved
in ¼ pint/150 ml/½ cup hot
water

1 rounded tsp arrowroot powder
dissolved in 1 tbsp water

Potassium salt

Freshly ground black pepper

1. These are the very small variety
2. See page 25

## Instructions

Trim and wash the greens. Cut them across into thick ribbons. Put a large stir-fry pan or saucepan over a medium heat. When hot add 2 tbsp olive oil and the greens. Stir well, then add the cold water and cover the pan. Turn the heat down to medium-low, cook for 5 minutes then season with potassium salt, stir and check that the water has not all evaporated. (If it has, add a little more). Replace the lid, cook for another 5 minutes then fast-boil away any remaining liquid. Remove from the heat; keep warm.

Bring a kettle of water to the boil then pour it over the rice noodles and leave to soak for 2 minutes. Drain then cover with cold water and drain again.

Put a frying pan (skillet) over a medium heat; when hot add 2 tbsp olive oil. Briefly sear the scallops on either side in the hot oil and remove. Pour the miso and hot water into the pan, stir in the dissolved arrowroot, return the scallops to the pan and simmer for about 5 minutes. Stir in the parsley and soya cream and remove from the heat. Keep warm.

Heat 2 tbsp olive oil in a stir-fry pan over a high heat, then add the soaked rice noodles. Stir-fry for about 20 seconds then add the greens, combine gently and pour into a warm serving dish. Pour the scallops and their sauce on top, and use two forks to combine the scallops with the other ingredients. Season with black pepper and serve immediately.

## What It's Good For

Greens (collards) are a member of the cabbage family, and contain ingredients which help your liver to break down pollutants in your body, helping to lower your cancer risk. Greens are rich in chlorophyll (which helps to neutralize toxins in your intestines), and in calcium, iron and carotenes, a type of antioxidant which also has a protective effect against cancer. The calcium in green vegetables is much more *bioavailable* (easier to assimilate) than the calcium in milk, making greens a better source of calcium than milk.

# Grilled Chicken Nuggets Marinated in Ginger and Garlic

## Ingredients for each serving

One medium-sized chicken breast,
   boned and skinned

1 tbsp olive oil

2 tbsp tamari sauce

1 tsp fresh ginger, finely chopped

1 tsp fresh garlic, finely chopped

## Instructions

Cut the chicken breast into strips about half an inch wide. Whisk together the other ingredients in a bowl large enough to hold all the chicken.

Place the chicken in the bowl and ensure it is well coated with marinade.

Leave for several hours (preferably overnight), turning the chicken occasionally.

Remove the grid from the grill (broiler) pan. Line the pan with foil, then preheat the grill to its highest setting.

Roll up the chicken strips and thread them close together on a flat skewer. Lay the skewer over the grill pan and place under the hot grill.

Cook for about 5 minutes on each side or until the chicken is cooked through. Serve with salad in a piece of folded unleavened bread, or with rice or millet.

The remaining marinade can be poured over some cold, cooked rice or millet in a hot stir-fry pan. Simply toss and stir over a medium heat, with a little extra water if necessary, until the grains are heated through.

## What It's Good For

Chicken is a good source of protein, and low in animal fat. While some therapeutic diets restrict protein for a while, it is important to remember that your liver cannot detoxify your blood unless it receives enough protein to manufacture essential enzymes. People with chronic fatigue syndrome especially need to avoid very low protein diets. When cooking chicken in this way, cut off any charred, blackened pieces and do not eat them. They contain toxic compounds. This method is better than barbecuing, as much less burnt smoke settles on the meat.

# Side Dishes and Accompaniments

If you have children who dislike vegetables, this could be simply because they don't like them boiled. After all, most children like canned vegetable soups, so it could simply be a matter of how they're served. Try chopping them very small and adding them to baked rice or braising them with succulent onion. Or make them into colourful, crunchy salads. Give the dish an interesting name like "Batman Stew".

# Southern Sweet Potato Bread

## Ingredients for 6-8 servings

1 medium-to large orange sweet potato, cooked and peeled

100 g/3½ ounces soya (soy) flour

100 g3½ ounces finely-ground yellow polenta meal

100 ml/3½ fluid oz soya (soy) milk

2 tbsp sunflower oil

1 heaped tsp potassium baking powder

## Instructions

Preheat the oven to gas mark 5.

All sweet potatoes have a purplish skin. The only way to tell if the flesh is orange is to scrape one gently with a fingernail. When preparing for this recipe, leave the potato whole, prick it all over with a sharp knife or fork, then steam for about 45 minutes or until soft. Or you could steam it for 20 minutes in a microwave instead.

Roughly chop the cooked, peeled sweet potato and put it in a food processor with all the other ingredients. Using the blade attachment, whizz the mixture until smooth, then transfer it to a small oiled loaf tin and bake for 40 minutes or until beginning to brown on top.

Serve cut into hunks with New England Baked Beans (page 81) and other bean dishes.

## What It's Good For

Both yellow polenta and sweet potatoes with orange-coloured flesh are rich in powerful antioxidants known as carotenes (similar to beta-carotene) and so can help to prevent cancer. This delicious sweet moist bread is best served freshly made and warm. Any leftovers can be wrapped in foil once cold. Reheat in the foil in a moderate oven for 10 minutes.

# Warm Salad of Grilled Vegetables with Lemon Zest

## Ingredients for 4 servings

2 medium onions, cut in four

2 sweet (bell) peppers, one red one
    green, deseeded and cut in four

4 medium tomatoes, halved

1 lemon

1 green chilli pepper, deseeded
    and finely chopped

1 handful Greek olives (black)

2 tbsp capers

1 tbsp coriander leaves (cilantro),
    coarsely chopped

Extra-virgin olive oil

## Instructions

Preheat the grill (broiler) to its highest setting.

Thread the onion quarters, sweet pepper pieces and tomato halves on skewers, brush liberally with olive oil and place under the grill (broiler) for 10 minutes, turning and brushing again with oil occasionally until the vegetables are beginning to tinge brown.

Meanwhile grate the zest off the lemon, then make a dressing by juicing the lemon and whisking the juice with 4 tbsp olive oil.

Add the zest to the dressing, together with the finely chopped chilli pepper and the capers.

When the vegetables are ready, slip them off the skewers, pour the dressing over them and ensure they are thoroughly coated.

Serve warm or tepid, sprinkled with the Greek olives and chopped coriander.

## What It's Good For

One of the major cancer-fighting flavonoids found in onions is quercetin, which also helps to fight allergies and prevent cataracts. Lemon peel is rich in the flavonoids hesperidin, which fights varicose veins and fluid retention by preventing blood vessel walls from getting thin and leaky, and nobiletin, which has anti-inflammatory action and helps the liver to process toxins. Lemon juice and sweet peppers are very rich in the powerful antioxidant vitamin C. Vitamin C is also needed for strong, healthy skin and blood vessels.

# Baked Rice Dishes

## Lemon Baked Rice

### Ingredients for 4 servings

300 ml/½ pint/1 cup organic brown rice (pour the rice into a measuring jug to measure the quantity) soaked for 6 hours or more in 600 ml/1 pint/2 cups water

Half a fresh lemon (preferably unwaxed*)

2 medium onions thinly sliced into half-rings

1 handful sunflower seeds

8 tbsp extra virgin olive oil

Potassium salt

Black pepper

*If not unwaxed, scrub the lemon in very hot water with detergent to remove as much pesticide-treated wax as possible.

### Instructions

Leaving the rice in its soaking water, bring to the boil in a lidded saucepan then simmer very gently for 20-25 minutes, until just tender. Quickly tip the rice into a large sieve to drain off any remaining water (save it for soup or stock as it is very rich in vitamins) then tip the rice straight back in the pan, replace the lid and leave the rice undisturbed for at least 5 minutes.

Preheat the oven to 190°C/375°F/gas mark 5.

Heat the oil in a large frying pan or stir-fry pan and fry the onions over a high heat until they are beginning to turn brown and crispy. (You will probably need to do this in two batches to avoid over-crowding the pan, which will create too much steam.)

Cut the half lemon into four pieces and pick out all the pips. Whizz the lemon pieces in a food processor until finely chopped. Fold the cooked onions, chopped lemon and the sunflower seeds into the brown rice, and season with potassium salt and pepper.

Put the rice in a casserole dish with a well-fitting lid, and bake for 40 minutes.

## What It's Good For

This dish is very rich in cancer-fighting flavonoid antioxidants. One of the major flavonoids found in onions is quercetin, which is especially helpful in fighting allergies and has been shown to help prevent cataracts. Lemon peel is rich in the flavonoids hesperidin, which fights varicose veins and fluid retention by preventing blood vessel walls from getting thin and leaky, and nobiletin, which has anti-inflammatory action and helps the liver to process toxins. Brown rice is an excellent source of B vitamins.

# Walnut and Mushroom Baked Rice

## Ingredients for 3-4 servings

*In this recipe a cup is an ordinary teacup*

2 cups cooked brown rice

1 medium carrot, grated

50 g/2 ounces/½ cup walnuts coarsely ground in food processor

1/4 lb mushrooms, diced

1 onion, cut in four

2 sticks celery, roughly cut into segments

1 green (bell) pepper, cut into 8 pieces

4 tbsp olive oil

A few leaves of fresh basil, chopped, or 1/2 tsp dried basil

Tamari sauce

Ground black pepper

## Instructions

Preheat the oven to 190°C/375°F/gas mark 5.

Process the onion, celery and green pepper together in a food processor until finely chopped. Place a large saucepan, or preferably a stir-fry pan, over a moderate to high heat, and when hot, add 2 tbsp olive oil, followed by the onion, celery and green pepper mixture and the grated carrot. Stir-fry for five minutes until the mixture begins to soften, then take off the heat and transfer the contents to a bowl.

Clean and dry the pan then replace over a medium-high heat and add the chopped mushrooms. Stir-fry without oil for a minute to dry them out a little, then add the oil and continue to stir-fry until golden brown.

Take off the heat, replace the vegetables in the pan, and mix in the chopped walnuts, basil, pepper and a few dashes of tamari sauce. Finally fold the grains in gently, ensuring that they do not break up.

Transfer the contents to an oiled loaf tin, smooth and press down evenly with a fork, cover with foil and bake for about 40 minutes.

### Variations

Use cooked buckwheat or millet instead of brown rice, or include a tablespoon of wild rice.

## More Ideas

The combination of walnuts with brown rice in this recipe yields substantial amounts of protein, so this dish could just be served with a salad or a portion of braised vegetables, and perhaps some garlic mushrooms.

It provides a very broad spread of nutrients, from B vitamins (brown rice) to beta carotene (carrots), chromium (mushrooms), and vitamin C (peppers). Other beneficial items include fluid retention-fighting coumarin (celery) and allergy-fighting quercetin (onions).

# Baked Red Cabbage with Apple and Garlic

## Ingredients for 4 servings

½ red cabbage, finely shredded

1 small, full-flavoured sweet apple, cored and thinly sliced

1 small onion, chopped

2 tbsp extra virgin olive oil

2 tbsp apple juice

1 tbsp raisins

2 cloves garlic, crushed or chopped

Black pepper

## Instructions

Preheat the oven to 160°C/325°F/gas mark 3.

Heat the oil in a stir-fry pan or large, heavy-bottomed saucepan, and stir-fry the onion gently until softened.

Add the apple and garlic and then the shredded cabbage, stirring continuously until it has shrunk a little. Then remove from the heat, stir in the raisins, put the mixture in a casserole dish, pour over the apple juice, season with black pepper, cover tightly and cook for one hour.

Serve with roast organic chicken and Creamed Potatoes (page 77) or with a stuffed Potato Pancake (page 57).

## What It's Good For

Members of the cabbage family are known to contain more anti-cancer substances than any other vegetables. And as a general rule, the more brightly-coloured a vegetable, the more free radical fighters it also contains in the form of flavonoids and carotenes. So, apart from being absolutely delicious, especially in this recipe, red cabbage is also extremely good for you!

# Vegetable Rösti Pancakes

## Ingredients for 2 servings

1 medium waxy potato, cut in four

1 medium carrot, cut into several segments

1 medium courgette (zucchini), cut into several segments

3 tbsp olive oil

1 tbsp soya or buckwheat flour

Black pepper

## Instructions

Grate all the vegetable pieces together, using a food processor, or coarsely grate them by hand. Season with black pepper. Do not add any form of salt to the vegetables, as this will make them release liquid.

The grated vegetables must be cooked immediately as potatoes discolour quickly when grated.

Heat the oil in a large frying pan (skillet) over a medium heat. Divide the grated vegetables into four portions. Form two portions into a round shape with your hands. Put them in the frying pan, and gently flatten them into thinnish pancakes, pressing with the edge of a spatula. (The edges can remain ragged.)

Cook for 1-2 minutes until the edges are turning golden and crispy, then remove the pancakes with a spatula and carefully slide them one at a time on to a small plate, put another plate on top, invert and slide back into the hot pan to cook the other side. Once cooked keep in a warm place until ready to serve. Repeat with the remaining portions.

Serve as a light snack with apple sauce (see page 130) or as a vegetable accompaniment, or cold as part of a buffet meal.

## What It's Good For

Taking only a few minutes to make, these succulent little pancakes are a delicious and unusual way to serve vegetables. Carrots are rich in antioxidant carotenes, especially beta carotene. Potatoes and courgettes are a good source of potassium and many vitamins and minerals.

# Garlic Potatoes Corfu Style

**Ingredients for 4 servings**

4 large potatoes, peeled

4 cloves of garlic, chopped

100 ml extra virgin olive oil

1 tsp chopped fresh rosemary

Boiling water

Potassium salt

Freshly ground black pepper

**Instructions**

Preheat the oven to 200°C/400°F/gas mark 6.

Cut the potatoes into large dice or thick slices and place in a shallow oven-proof dish. Sprinkle with seasoning, followed by chopped garlic and rosemary, then pour in the olive oil. Top up with enough boiling water to almost cover the potatoes, cover the dish with foil and place in the oven.

Cook for 45 minutes, then remove the foil and cook for a further 30 minutes uncovered, or until the water has evaporated and the potatoes are crisp and golden on top and tender in the middle. Drain off the excess oil, which is full of flavour and can be saved for another dish.

As the level of oil drops with the evaporation of the water, all the potatoes are coated with the oil and the wonderful flavours of the garlic and rosemary.

*Variations*

In Corfu, this dish is often made with a selection of different vegetables: courgettes (zucchini), carrots, onions and tomatoes, for example.

## What It's Good For

Eating this dish, you won't be able to help dreaming of sun-drenched Mediterranean shores! Potatoes are rich in potassium and minerals, and although only raw garlic has anti-bacterial and anti-fungal effects in the intestines, cooked garlic still has many beneficial effects on arteries, blood pressure, cholesterol, diabetes and the elimination of toxic (heavy) metals from the body.

# Onion Marmalade

## Ingredients for 3-4 servings

450 g/1 lb onions, peeled

2 tbsp extra virgin olive oil

Potassium salt

## Instructions

Using a mandolin type appliance (with a spiked holder for the onions so that you don't slice into your fingers!) slice the onions thinly, then place them in a stir-fry pan with the oil over a medium heat. Using a large spoon, break up the onion slices into rings, and stir-fry until well-coated. Put a lid on the pan, and leave the onions to sweat over a very low heat for 30 minutes. Remove the lid, add potassium salt and stir-fry the onions with the lid off for 10 minutes to reduce any excess moisture. The onions should be soft and melting.

Reheat before serving. This is especially good with fish and steamed potatoes.

## What It's Good For

The therapeutic value of the humble onion is often forgotten in favour of its famous cousin garlic. Onions are a rich source of the so-called "anti-allergy" flavonoid quercetin. This flavonoid is very similar to the drug disodium chromoglycate, which is given to allergy sufferers to switch off their symptoms. Like the drug, quercetin has the ability to inhibit the release of histamine, which is responsible for allergic symptoms and asthma attacks. Onions are especially beneficial to diabetics, since they are as effective in lowering blood sugar as some prescription drugs.

# Polenta with Olives and Sun-Dried Tomatoes

## Ingredients for 4-6 servings

250 g/9 ounces yellow polenta meal, preferably coarse-ground

1½ litres/2½ pints/5¼ cups boiling water

50 g/2 ounces/1 cup white mushrooms, diced small and fried for 2 minutes in 1 tbsp olive oil

8 large green olives, stoned and cut in four

15 g/½ ounce/1 heaped tbsp sun-dried tomatoes, thinly shredded

Potassium salt

Freshly ground black pepper

To ensure that your polenta turns out right, these instructions should be followed even if the packet gives different quantities of water or cooking times.

## Instructions

Pour the polenta meal and potassium salt into a saucepan containing the boiling water, whisking it rapidly as you do so to prevent lumps from forming. Turn the heat down to a gentle simmer and stir the polenta from time to time with a large wooden spoon, leaving the lid off the pan. The polenta is not ready yet even if it thickens and starts to sputter—keep turning the heat down until the sputtering is minimal. Keep stirring until the mixture is gelatinous and stiff. This takes about 40 minutes.

When the polenta is ready, combine the diced mushrooms, olive pieces and sun-dried tomato shreds and fold them evenly and very gently into the polenta. Spoon the polenta into an oiled shallow dish large enough to result in a layer half to one inch thick when the polenta is spread out in it. Spoon in the polenta and then use the back of a fork to get the layer as even as possible.

Cover the dish with a tea towel and allow it to cool, then refrigerate until chilled. When you are ready to serve the polenta, divide it into portions, carefully remove them from the dish, and fry on each side in hot olive oil until golden and crispy. Serve with Ratatouille (see page opposite).

## What It's Good For

Polenta is yellow cornmeal, rich in anti-cancer carotenes, and also essential polyunsaturated oils, vitamin E and complex carbohydrates. Polenta cooked in this way is very versatile, and In Italy it is often used as a substitute for pasta.

# Ratatouille

## Ingredients for 4 servings

1 medium-sized aubergine (eggplant) cut into large dice

1x400 g/14 ounce can of Italian plum tomatoes

2 medium-sized courgettes (zucchini) sliced about ¼ inch thick

1 medium-sized green (bell) pepper, cut into about 20 pieces

4 cloves garlic, peeled and flattened with the side of a large knife

4 tbsp extra virgin olive oil

1 tsp mixed dried Provençale herbs

Potassium salt

Freshly ground black pepper

## Instructions

Heat the oil in a large, heavy-bottomed saucepan over a medium heat. When hot, put all the vegetables in the pan. Stir, add the herbs and potassium salt, then cover the pan, bring to the boil, turn the heat down and sweat the vegetables over a low heat for one hour, stirring occasionally.

Remove the lid and check the consistency. If necessary, boil the ratatouille rapidly with the lid off to reduce the sauce until you have a "thick stew" consistency. The vegetables should not swim in liquid.

Stir in the freshly ground black pepper and serve hot or cold. This goes especially well with polenta (see page 94).

## What It's Good For

This old southern French peasant dish could be one of the reasons why the Mediterranean peoples have a much better life expectancy than people in the UK or North America. Rich in heart-disease preventing vitamin C and flavonoid and carotene antioxidants, this kind of food is just perfect for good body maintenance. Even the rosemary herb used in Provençale cookery contains antioxidants! I have recommended canned tomatoes here because they are almost always a rich, deep red, which indicates a good content of natural carotenes.

# Cauliflower in Cream Sauce

## Ingredients for 2-4 servings

1 medium head of cauliflower

425 ml/¾ pint/1½ cups water

2 tbsp groundnut oil

1 rounded dessertspoon brown rice flour

2 tbsp soya (soy) cream

Potassium salt

## Special Equipment

A steaming basket

## Instructions

Bring the water to the boil in a large saucepan which can be used for steaming. Divide the cauliflower into small florets. Wash thoroughly and place in a steaming basket inside the pan of boiling water. Steam over a medium heat with the lid on for 10-15 minutes, until tender.

Put the oil in another saucepan over a gentle heat and stir in the rice flour. When the cauliflower is cooked, drain the cooking water into a jug, add some potassium salt, and keep the cauliflower warm. Whisk the hot cooking water gradually into the oil and rice flour mixture until evenly blended and thickened. Simmer over a low heat for 5 minutes, stirring from time to time.

Add the soya cream and gently warm through without boiling. Pour the sauce over the cauliflower, toss so that it is well coated, and serve immediately.

## What It's Good For

Like broccoli, cabbage and brussels sprouts, cauliflower belongs to the Brassica family of vegetables— famous for its ability to fight cancer-causing chemicals. The anti-cancer substances in these vegetables include indoles, phenols, coumarins and isothiocyanates. They provide raw materials for your liver to get rid of cancer-causing pollutants, and block the effects of cancer-causing compounds. In women, they help the liver to break down the hormone oestrogen once it has done its job. Problems in breaking down this hormone are known to encourage breast cancer. It is well worth consuming a member of the Brassica family every day of the week, and this delicious recipe will make it a real pleasure.

# Aromatic Carrots with Garlic and Shallots

## Ingredients for 4 servings

4 medium carrots, cut into julienne strips

2 medium shallots, peeled and roughly diced

4 cloves garlic, peeled and crushed

2 tbsp extra virgin olive oil

A pinch of your favourite mixed dried herbs (e.g. tarragon and thyme)

Potassium salt

Freshly ground black pepper

## Instructions

Heat the oil over a medium heat in a heavy-bottomed saucepan, and add the shallots. Cook until beginning to soften, then stir in the garlic and carrot strips. Ensure they are coated with oil.

Season with potassium salt and a sprinkling of herbs, then add four tbsp water, turn the heat down to its lowest setting, and cover the pan tightly.

Cook for 25 minutes, after which time the carrots should be tender.

If there are more than a couple of tablespoons of cooking juices in the bottom of the pan, turn up the heat to fast-boil it until reduced. Gently turn the carrots to moisten them with the juices, then season with freshly ground black pepper and serve immediately.

*Variation*

Try mixing the carrots with quartered brussels sprouts. This cooking method (braising) can also be used with shredded cabbage and dwarf green beans.

## What It's Good For

This is a wonderful nutrient-conserving method of cooking carrots, and so delicious that you will never again want to cook them any other way! Carrots are rich in antioxidant carotenes, especially beta carotene. Because people who eat a lot of carrots are most highly protected from lung cancer, scientists have carried out research giving beta carotene supplements to smokers to find out whether these supplements have the same effect. It appears that they are not nearly so effective as carrots themselves, so carrots clearly contain other nutrients which do the job.

# Potato Cakes *Grand Prix*

So called because they are so fast to make!

## Ingredients

Allow 1 medium starchy potato for each serving of 2 potato cakes

Olive oil for frying

Potassium salt

## Special Equipment

A round "cooking ring" or pastry cutter with a diameter of about 3 inches for each potato cake.

## Instructions

Peel and coarsely grate the potatoes, putting the gratings into a bowl of cold water. Using your hands, remove two handfuls of grated potato from the water, squeeze out the excess water and lay the grated potato on a clean tea towel. Fold the tea towel over and press the potatoes again to dry them as much as possible.

Put a large frying pan (skillet) over a medium heat and coat the bottom with a thin layer of olive oil. When the oil is hot, put the cooking rings into the pan, and drop grated potato into each ring, pressing down gently so that you get a cake with a thickness of about ¼ inch. Drizzle a teaspoon of olive oil over the potato cakes, then sprinkle with a pinch of potassium salt. Cook for five minutes, or until the bottom of the cakes is crisp and golden, then carefully remove the rings, turn the cakes over with flat tongs and cook the other side without the ring.

Drain the cakes on absorbent kitchen paper and keep them warm while you cook the next batch. Serve with apple sauce or as a vegetable accompaniment.

## What It's Good For

Potatoes are often thought of as a "fattening" food, but in fact are not at all high in calories. A medium-sized potato provides only about 110 Calories. It is the butter and sauces potatoes are served with, and the oil they are fried in which can make them fattening. Potatoes are rich in potassium and also contain some protein and a little vitamin C.

# Braised Cornish Vegetables

## Ingredients for each serving

1 medium potato

1 piece of swede (rutabaga) the same size as the potato

Half a medium onion

1 tbsp extra virgin olive oil

Potassium salt

Pepper

## Instructions

These vegetables are the traditional filling inside a Cornish pasty, minus the meat. They make a succulent and delicious vegetable accompaniment which I find extremely more-ish!

Finely dice all the vegetables, then sweat them over a very low heat in a lidded pan with the olive oil for 45 minutes, stirring occasionally and adding a tablespoon of water if they show any sign of sticking to the bottom of the pan. Serve with grilled fish or spiced bean röstis or roast organic chicken.

## What It's Good For

Swedes (known in Cornwall as turnips) are a sadly under-appreciated vegetable whose delicious sweetness perfectly complements potatoes and onions. Like cauliflower and cabbage, they are a member of the Brassica family which is famous for its anti-cancer benefits.

# German Potato Salad

## Ingredients for 4 servings

1 kg/2 pounds waxy potatoes

4 spring onions (scallions) finely
    sliced

6 tbsp extra virgin olive oil

4 tbsp mayonnaise (see page 132)

3 tbsp additive-free cider vinegar
    or white wine vinegar

1 tbsp capers, chopped

Potassium salt

Freshly-ground black pepper

## Instructions

Steam the potatoes whole in their jackets until just tender (about 30-40 minutes).

Whisk together the oil, vinegar, salt and pepper in a large bowl, then stir in the spring onion slices and chopped capers. Leave to one side for the flavours to blend together.

When the potatoes are cooked, hold them on a fork (so that you don't burn your fingers) and peel them with a small knife.

Once peeled, cut them into medium-sized dice and, while still warm, put them them in the bowl containing the oil and vinegar dressing. (Whisk it again first if it has separated).

Gently turn the potatoes in the dressing until they are well coated. Leave to one side for at least one hour so that the potatoes can absorb the dressing.

Just before you are ready to serve the potato salad, spoon in the mayonnaise and turn the potatoes around in it gently until they are evenly coated.

## What It's Good For

By adding the mayonnaise after the potatoes have soaked up the vinaigrette, they will only need a light coating and yet will still be succulent and full of flavour.

The main benefits of this recipe come from the extra virgin olive oil and the potatoes, which are rich in potassium and also contain a little protein, including the anti-herpes amino acid lysine.

N.B. Sometimes anti-candida diets forbid vinegar because it contains yeasts and most Candida sufferers have a yeast allergy. However, those in vinegar (and miso) are natural yeasts, and are much less likely to cause allergic reactions than the commercial yeasts found in wine, beer, bread, pizza dough etc. If it does, use lemon or lime juice instead.

# Diced Fried New Potatoes and Courgettes with a Pesto Coating

## Ingredients for 4 servings

4 medium-sized new potatoes, unpeeled, diced small

2 medium-sized courgettes, diced

1 large handful fresh basil leaves

25 g/1 ounce/1 small handful walnuts or pine nuts

4 tbsp extra virgin olive oil, plus

Ordinary olive oil for frying

1 clove garlic

Potassium salt

## Instructions

Put enough olive oil to form a ¼-inch layer in a large frying pan (skillet) over a medium to high heat. When hot, add the diced potatoes but do not overcrowd the pan. If necessary, cook them in two batches. Stir and turn over the potatoes occasionally to ensure that they cook as evenly as possible. When done, they should be golden and slightly crispy. This should take about 10 minutes. Remove the potatoes from the pan with a slotted spoon, drain them on absorbent kitchen paper and keep them warm.

Put the pan back over the heat and cook the diced courgettes in the same way, adding a little more oil if necessary. The courgettes should take about 5 minutes to cook. When done, remove them from the pan, drain them briefly on absorbent kitchen paper and keep warm.

Make the pesto coating by putting 4 tbsp olive oil in a blender with the garlic, fresh basil, walnuts or pine nuts and potassium salt. Whizz until smooth and creamy.

Combine the potatoes and courgettes in a bowl and spoon in the pesto sauce. Fold together until the vegetables are thoroughly coated and serve immediately. This goes well with the Plaice Meunière recipe on page 71.

## What It's Good For

In herbal medicine, basil was traditionally used against nervous irritability and to treat nausea and vomiting. It is little used by herbalists today. It also has anti-fungal, anti-bacterial and anti-parasitic properties, which are useful for people suffering from candidiasis and other imbalances in their intestinal bacteria. Walnuts are sometimes known as "brain food", perhaps because they look like tiny brains! They are rich in essential polyunsaturated oils, protein, vitamin E, calcium, iron and zinc.

# Mini Rainbow Salads

## Ingredients

Any combination of the following, depending on how many people you are catering for.

Finely grated swede (rutabaga)

Grated carrot

Grated raw beetroot (beet) or cooked beetroot cut into matchsticks

Tomatoes, thinly sliced

Grated mooli radish*

sweet peppers (red, green, orange) finely diced

*Long, white "icicle" radishes

## Instructions

Put in layers of contrasting coloured ingredients in small ramekin dishes or timbale moulds, starting with a slice of tomato. Press down gently.

Turn out on to a bed of lettuce or alfalfa sprouts (or a mixture of both) and spoon vinaigrette dressing (see page 103) flavoured with thinly sliced spring onion (scallion) over the top.

(see page 103)

## What It's Good For

I have extolled the virtues of the humble swede elsewhere in this book, but most people don't know that it is truly delicious eaten raw. I discovered this when I travelled to Iceland and was given a simple but exquisite dish of poached white fish with onions sweated in butter and a salad of grated raw swede and vinegar.

# Vinaigrette Salad Dressing

**Ingredients for**
**125 ml/4½ fluid oz/½ cup**

6 tbsp extra virgin olive oil

2 tbsp cider vinegar or wine
    vinegar

1 tsp English mustard powder

Potassium salt

Freshly ground black pepper

## Instructions

Mix the mustard powder to a smooth paste with a little of the vinegar in a bowl, then, using a fork or small whisk, beat in a little oil followed by the rest of the oil and then the remaining ingredients.

This makes a basic vinaigrette. You can add any other ingredients you like, such as fresh or dried chopped herbs or gherkins, capers, raw garlic or finely sliced spring onion (scallion). Whisk the vinaigrette again just before serving.

If you are serving vinaigrette with a green salad, do not put it on the salad until the last minute.

## What It's Good For

The main benefits of this recipe come from extra virgin olive oil, which has been in the news recently since scientists found that it can help to prevent our brain processes from deteriorating as we get older.

N.B. Sometimes anti-candida diets forbid vinegar because it contains yeasts and most Candida sufferers have a yeast allergy. However, those in vinegar (and miso) are natural yeasts, much less likely to cause allergic reactions than the commercial yeasts found in wine, beer, bread, pizza dough and so on. If it does, use lemon or lime juice instead.

# Three-Bean Salad

## Ingredients for each serving

2 tbsp cooked chickpeas

2 tbsp cooked red kidney beans

2 tbsp cooked black-eyed beans

1 spring onion (scallion), thinly sliced

1 stick celery, sliced

1 tbsp fresh chopped parsley

Half a green sweet (bell) pepper, thinly sliced

Half a red sweet (bell) pepper, thinly sliced

2 tbsp vinaigrette dressing (see page 103)

Potassium salt

Freshly ground black pepper

## Instructions

Combine all the ingredients and stir again just before serving.

This salad is ideal as part of a packed lunch together with German Potato Salad (page 100) and cold Falafel (page 54).

## What It's Good For

Beans are rich in protein, filling, and delicious in salads. They are ideal in packed lunches because they contain a type of dietary fibre which slows down your absorption of carbohydrate from your meal. This helps to keep you feeling full for longer. Sweet peppers are rich in vitamin C, and raw onion has some of the anti-fungal and anti-bacterial properties of raw garlic.

# Potato Gnocci (Italian potato dumplings)

## Ingredients for about 40 small Gnocci (2 servings)

400 g/14 ounces/4 medium waxy
    potatoes*

50 g/1¾ ounces/2 tbsp potato flour
    (potato starch)

Potassium salt

*You must use waxy potatoes for this or the gnocci will not hold together when cooked. If unsure, choose varieties sold as "salad" potatoes.

## Special Equipment

A potato press

## Instructions

Steam the potatoes in their jackets until tender (about 30 minutes). Hold them on a fork (so that you don't burn your fingers) and peel them with a small knife.

Put a large pan of unsalted water over a high heat and bring to the boil. Put the potatoes through a potato press then work the potato flour into them using a fork. Once the two ingredients are evenly blended, change to a rubber spatula and mash to a paste. Turn the paste out on to a board or worktop, and knead the mixture, using your hands, until it is smooth and pliable. Divide in half.

Again using your hands, roll this dough into a long sausage shape with a diameter of about half an inch. Cut each roll into 10 segments, then briefly roll each segment between your hands to round it into an oval shape. Press the centre with the end of a fork to make little indentations which will help the gnocci to hold their sauce later on.

As you prepare the gnocci, put them on a small plate then gently slide them off the plate into the gently boiling water. These small gnocci should rise to the surface after about 40 seconds of boiling. After they have risen, count another 20 seconds, then remove them from the water with a slotted spoon. You can also make larger gnocci and they will take a little longer to rise.

## Ways to serve Gnocci

Topped with tomato, mushroom and olive sauce (page 75) and a dollop of Garlic Crème (page 129).

Folded gently into braised vegetables.

Warmed through then coated with pesto sauce (page 101).

Lightly coated with olive oil then sprinkled with a liberal topping of grated goat's or sheep's cheese and placed under a hot grill (broiler) until golden and bubbling.

# Millet with Crunchy Salad Vegetables and Fruit Pieces

## Ingredients for 2 servings

Millet grains measured up to the 120 ml/4 fluid oz/½ cup mark in a measuring jug

200 ml/7 fluid oz/generous ¾ cup water

2 tbsp each of chopped, finely diced and/or grated salad vegetables: carrots, celery, sweet (bell) peppers, watercress, cucumber, mint, radishes, spring onion (scallion)

One apple or orange

4 tbsp vinaigrette dressing (see page 103)

1 tbsp lemon juice if using apple

## Instructions

Toast the millet grains in a dry frying pan (skillet) over a medium heat for about 10 minutes, or until they give off a roasted aroma and begin to change colour. Transfer them to a saucepan, add the water, bring to the boil and simmer over a low heat for 30 minutes.

Remove from the heat. Remove the lid, add 1 tbsp water, stir briefly, then replace the lid and leave undisturbed until cool.

Cut the apple into small dice, and place in a bowl of water with the lemon juice (to prevent discolouring).

Alternatively, if using an orange, cut into segments as described on page 113.

Shortly before serving, fluff up the millet with a fork, whisk the vinaigrette and stir it into the millet with the vegetables. Finally fold in the fruit pieces. This dish is excellent in a packed lunch.

*Variation*

You could use cooked brown rice or buckwheat instead of millet.

## What It's Good For

Millet is a very ancient grain, and has been cultivated for longer than rice, wheat and rye. It is a rich source of many vitamins and minerals and is one of the best sources of the mineral silica, which is needed for strong bones and teeth. People with food intolerances rarely have a problem with millet, as it is gluten free and easy to digest. It can safely be added to any hypoallergenic diet. Millet is also said to have anti-fungal properties and therefore may be able to help people with intestinal candiasis.

# Super Sweets

I guarantee you will be amazed at how easy it is to make delicious sweet dishes without sugar. Those who try to sell us sugar insist there's no difference between the stuff in packets and the natural sugars in fruits. As far as your body is concerned, this is not true. Sugar bound up with the dietary fibre in fruit is absorbed much more slowly into your blood than added sugar, resulting in a more gradual rise in the hormone insulin.

But packet sugar (as well as honey and syrups) can produce high insulin levels in your body very quickly. Too much insulin encourages fatty deposits on artery walls, fluid retention, and is also stressful to your kidneys.

# Little Castagnacci (Italian chestnut cakes)

## Ingredients to make 12

200 g/7 ounces/1 cup chestnut flour

260 ml/scant ½ pint/1 cup water

Extra virgin olive oil

40g raisins

40g washed and dried brazil nuts, roughly chopped

1 tbsp fresh rosemary, chopped

## Instructions

Preheat the oven to 190°C/375°F/gas mark 5.

Stir the water into the chestnut flour a little at a time until you have a smooth paste with a "soft dropping" consistency. Stir in the raisins and chopped brazil nuts, and 2 tbsp olive oil. Drop a teaspoon of olive oil into each of the wells of a well-oiled shallow bun or muffin tin, followed by tablespoons of the chestnut mixture to a depth of no more than half an inch. Smooth the tops flat with a fork, then sprinkle on a little chopped rosemary and olive oil. Bake for 25 minutes or until cracked on top, then allow to cool for at least 30 minutes before serving. These cakes do not keep well and are best eaten within a day or two.

*Variation*

This recipe is best made with chestnut flour, but it is possible to make something similar with boiled, peeled chestnuts, or with dried chestnuts which have been soaked in hot water overnight and then boiled until soft. Blend the chestnuts in a food processor with enough water to achieve a slightly stiff consistency before adding the other ingredients

## What It's Good For

This is an adaptation of an ancient Italian recipe—crunchy on the outside, sweet and moist in the centre. Chestnut flour is available from health food stores, or in the event of difficulty see page 23. Selenium-rich brazil nuts can help to prevent heart attacks and cancer, and to protect you against many pollutants. Always wash brazil nuts thoroughly before use, as they are prone to develop mould soon after shelling. Chestnuts are low in oil, and are nutritionally quite similar to grains such as corn or rice. They are rich in potassium, magnesium and iron.

# Chewy Chocolate Truffles

## Ingredients to make 15 truffles

115 g/4 ounces dried dates

40 g/1½ ounces cocoa powder

55 g/2 ounces coarsely-chopped nuts

## Instructions

Put the dates in a small saucepan, add just enough water to cover them and bring to the boil. Simmer on the lowest heat with the lid on for 15 minutes or until soft, then transfer the dates to a bowl.

Stir in some of the cocoa powder and mash it into the dates with the back of a tablespoon. Repeat until most of the cocoa powder has been incorporated, and you have a stiff, dough-like consistency. Tip half the chopped nuts plus the remaining cocoa powder on to a board, scrape out the dough and add it to them, then, using your hands, knead these remaining ingredients into the dough.

Roll the dough into a long sausage about half an inch or less in diameter, and cut it into 15 segments. (If necessary dust with more cocoa powder to prevent it sticking to the board.) Using your hands, roll each segment into a ball, flatten slightly, place in a fondant case and sprinkle with more chopped nuts.

Alternatively, make a slightly stickier mixture (using less cocoa powder), and roll the truffle balls in the chopped nuts so that they cling to them.

## What It's Good For

Chocaholics will love this recipe, which contains none of the fat and sugar which makes overindulgence in ordinary chocolate so harmful. Cocoa powder is rich in iron and magmesium. But do not use it if you suffer from breast lumps or cysts or any form of breast tenderness. Cocoa and chocolate contain caffeine-like compounds which seem to encourage breast problems in some women.

Dates are an excellent source of good quality dietary fibre, so these truffles can even help to keep your bowels working smoothly!

# Gourmet Marzipan

**Makes enough to cover 2 standard-size fruit cakes or to make 48 bouchées (mouth-size nibbles)**

<u>115 g/4 ounces dried dates</u>

<u>300 g/10½ ounces ground almonds/almond flour*</u>

<u>½ tsp natural vanilla essence</u>

*For this recipe, commercially ground almonds produce a smoother result than those home-ground in a food processor.

## Instructions

Put the dates in a small saucepan, add just enough water to cover them and bring to the boil. Simmer on the lowest heat with the lid on for 15 minutes or until soft. Transfer the dates to a bowl. Stir in the vanilla essence and some of the ground almonds. Mash them into the dates with the back of a tablespoon. Repeat until you have a stiff, dough-like consistency. Tip the remaining ground almonds on to a board, add the dough, then, using your hands, knead the remaining ground almonds into the dough.

The dough can be rolled out to the required dimensions for a cake (use more ground almonds to prevent the dough sticking to the board). First spread the cake with all-fruit apricot or cherry spread to hold the marzipan in place.

To make mouth-sized marzipan balls, roll the dough into sausages, cut off bite-size portions, and roll these into balls. These bouchées are delicious as they are or can be used to stuff prunes or dipped in melted bitter chocolate (with the aid of toothpicks to grip them). Place in fondant cases

*Variation*

Use unsulphured (dark brown) dried apricots or dried cherries instead of dates.

## What It's Good For

Dates are an excellent source of good quality dietary fibre, so this wonderful marzipan can even help to keep your bowels working smoothly. Do not consume marzipan or any nut-rich recipes if you suffer from herpes, since nuts are rich in arginine, an amino acid which can cause flare-ups of the herpes virus. Almonds are rich in calcium and magnesium and are a good source of protein.

# Baked Rice Pudding with Coconut Cream

## Ingredients for 4-6 servings

115 g/4 ounces/scant 1 cup unpolished sweet rice which has been soaked in water overnight then drained

1 litre carton soya (soy) milk

1 knob creamed coconut

1 handful raisins

2 tbsp almonds or cashew nuts, well-washed and finely chopped

Use cashew nuts instead of almonds if you prefer a sweeter flavour.

## Instructions

Preheat the oven to 175°C/325°F/gas mark 3.

Place the ingredients in a saucepan and bring to a gentle simmer, stirring until the creamed coconut has dissolved. Pour into a casserole dish placed on a baking tray, cover and bake in the oven for 2 hours. Check that the pudding does not boil over, and if necessary turn the heat down a fraction to prevent this. Remove the pudding after one hour to give it a good stir then replace it in the oven to finish cooking. You could also try cooking this in a saucepan on top of the stove if you wish, with the gas or electric ring on its lowest setting, and a heat diffuser under the pan if necessary. In this case a cast-iron enamelled pan would be best.

Serve hot or cold

- On its own as a delicious breakfast dish, perhaps with prunes,
- Or as a dessert on a shallow plate beside one of the following garnishes:
  Sliced sharon fruit or persimmon and banana.
  Reconstituted Hunza apricots (small dried apricots which are pale and very sweet in flavour).
  A small chestnut cake (page 108).

## What It's Good For

Sweet rice is also known as glutinous rice, and is an ingredient in many oriental sweet dishes. Unpolished sweet rice (which is a form of brown rice and is therefore rich in B vitamins and much more nutritious than the white version) is available from Infinity Foods (see page 163) in the UK. In this dish, the soya milk becomes condensed from long, slow cooking, giving you all the concentrated benefits of soy foods (see page 28). Creamed coconut contains coconut oil, which is good for people with post-viral chronic fatigue as it is rich in the anti-viral substance lauric acid.

# Kiwi Fruit Slices in Apple Jelly with Strawberry Coulis

## Ingredients for 4 servings

6 kiwi fruit, peeled and thinly
    sliced

200 g/½ lb/1½ cups sweet
    strawberries, chopped

275 ml/½ pint/1 cup apple juice
    plus 2 tbsp

1 rounded tbsp agar flakes

## Instructions

Sprinkle the agar flakes on the apple juice in a sauce-pan. Do not stir. Place the pan over a medium heat and bring to a gentle simmer. Simmer for 3-5 minutes, stirring occasionally until dissolved.

Arrange the kiwi fruit as evenly as possible in over-lapping layers in a shallow serving dish, saving the prettiest slices for the top layer. You could also place them in individual dishes or moulds. (First line the moulds with cling film to help you turn out the jellies without breaking.)

Spoon the apple juice gently over the fruit, until it is just covered with jelly. Sets quickly (about 30 minutes). Refrigerate once cool.

To make the coulis, place the chopped strawber-ries in a blender with 2 tbsp apple juice and whizz until smooth. Serve with the jelly and a dollop of sheep's yoghurt.

## What It's Good For

Kiwi fruit is one of the richest known sources of vitamin C. It is also one of the prettiest fruits once sliced. Agar is a flavourless natural gelling and thickening agent made from seaweed. The agar used in this recipe is Clearspring agar (see address on page 163). While many brands of agar (or agar-agar) are available in oriental shops, some are made by methods involving chemical extraction and bleaching. Clearspring and other macrobiotic agars are made by a traditional process. Agar can be used in jellies and aspics, and as a thickener.

# Banana Crème

## Ingredients for 2 servings

1 banana

100 g/3½ ounces/½ cup firm tofu

100 ml/3½ fluid oz soya (soy) milk

55 g/2 ounces/½ cup raw cashew
nut pieces, well washed and
drained

1 tbsp tahini (sesame paste)

2 tsp lemon juice

1 tsp natural vanilla extract

## Instructions

Whizz all the ingredients except the tahini in a food processor using the "S" blade, until they are well blended, then add the tahini and continue to whizz until the mixture is very smooth. (This could take up to 5 minutes processing).

Serve the Banana Crème on its own in small glass dishes, topped with peeled orange segments, or as a topping poured over pear slices or a banana cut in half lengthwise. Decorate with a sliced strawberry.

*To peel orange segments*

Cut the ends off a whole orange. Stand it up then cut the peel off in a downward direction, working all the way around the orange and removing the outer white pith and membrane as you cut.

Using the same knife, cut between each segment, on either side of the membrane separating it from the next segment. Go all the way around the orange like this. The V-shaped orange pieces should easily come out perfectly skinned.

## What It's Good For

Soya milk and tofu are rich sources of hormone-balancing isoflavones which help to prevent problems from excess or insufficient oestrogen, and excess testosterone. So a diet rich in tofu and other soya products can help to prevent menopausal hot flushes, breast cancer and prostate cancer. Cashew nuts are low in oil and rich in potassium and magnesium, iron and zinc. Raw cashews are liable to develop a little mould while in their packets, so must always be washed before use. Bananas are rich in many vitamins and minerals, especially potassium.

# Apple Custard

## Ingredients for 2 servings

150 ml/¼ pint/½ cup soya (soy) milk

4 tbsp apple sauce made as described on page 130

## Instructions

Put the apple sauce in a small saucepan over a medium heat and whisk in the soya milk. Keep whisking until the mixture thickens to the consistency of a thin custard.

*Variation*

Because of its higher pectin content, apple butter (see page 130) can be whipped with soya milk as described above, to make a slightly thicker, more frothy custard. The texture is slightly chalky, but you may enjoy it.

To make it, use only 1 tbsp apple butter to 150 ml soya milk and keep whisking until the result is thick and frothy.

## What It's Good For

Apple peel contains amazing nutritional value. It is very rich in cancer-preventing carotenes and flavonoids, as well as a type of soluble dietary fibre known as pectin. Pectin is a gelling agent used in jam-making, and is the reason why apple sauce can thicken soya milk in this recipe. Pectin can also help to treat constipation, and it binds to toxins in your intestines and helps your body eliminate them. Unfortunately, although the skin is the most nutritious part of the apple, it is also the part most liable to contain pesticides, so try to use organic apples if you can.

# Oat and Treacle Wedges

## Ingredients for 8 servings

115 g/4 ounces/generous 1 cup rolled oats

55 g/2 ounces/scant half cup sunflower seeds

55 g/2 ounces/half cup raisins

50 ml/2 fluid oz/4 tbsp groundnut oil

2 tbsp date purée made as described on page 109

1 tbsp blackstrap molasses

## Instructions

Preheat the oven to 180°C/350°F/gas mark 4.

Mix the dry ingredients in a bowl. Warm the date purée in a saucepan then stir in the molasses and oil.

Add the dry ingredients to the saucepan and stir until thoroughly incorporated.

Press the mixture evenly into an oiled 8-inch diameter sandwich tin and bake in the centre of the oven for 25-30 minutes.

Cut into 8 wedges while still warm and allow to cool completely before eating.

## What It's Good For

Oats are a great source of a type of soluble dietary fibre which helps you excrete cholesterol. They are also rich in B vitamins, and are one of the best dietary sources of magnesium. Dates are also rich in fibre and can be a great aid to regular bowel motions. Blackstrap molasses is a thick residue left from sugar processing, and contains all the minerals of the sugar cane or sugar beet left behind when white or brown sugar is produced: calcium, magnesium, iron, zinc and manganese to name just a few. Sunflower seeds are also rich in magnesium, as well as essential polyunsaturated oils.

# Fruity Almond Cookies

## Ingredients for 20 cookies

115 g/4 oz unsulphured dried apricots

110 g/4 oz ground almonds

50 g/4 oz soya flour

50 g/2 oz chopped mixed nuts

50 g/2 oz mixed dried fruit with peel

1 level teaspoon potassium baking powder

1 teaspoon natural vanilla extract

Water as required.

## Instructions

Preheat the oven to 180°C/350°F/gas mark 4.

Lightly oil a baking sheet. Dice the dried apricots, place them in a small saucepan and just cover with water. Bring to the boil and simmer very gently for 30 minutes. Add a little more water if necessary to prevent them drying out. Mix the dry ingredients together.

Once the apricots are cooked, purée them with a hand blender, adding a little more water if necessary to obtain a thick, smooth purée. Stir in the vanilla essence, then mix into the dry ingredients. Incorporate thoroughly, to achieve a thick, stiff paste.

Roll the paste into two long sausage shapes. Divide each roll into 10 segments. Roll each segment into a ball with your hands, press your hands together to flatten it, and place it on the baking sheet.

Bake in the preheated oven for 20 minutes. The cookies become stale after 24 hours but can be restored by gently warming under the grill.

## What It's Good For

Dried apricots are orange in colour if treated with sulphur dioxide. This additive is an intestinal irritant and can cause bloating and gas. Unsulphured apricots (from health food shops) are dark brown and much sweeter. Apricots are an excellent source of cancer-preventing carotenes, potassium and other minerals. Almonds are a great source of calcium and magnesium, iron, zinc and vitamin E and essential polyunsaturated oils. They are best avoided by people prone to cold sores and herpes, since (like other nuts) they are rich in the amino acid arginine, which can encourage herpes if eaten in large amounts.

# Exotic Warm Fruit Salad in Grape Juice

## Ingredients for 4 servings

1 peach, thinly sliced

1 small mango, skinned and chopped

1 kiwi fruit, peeled and sliced

2 slices fresh pineapple (or canned pineapple in juice, drained)

2 tbsp fresh or frozen (defrosted) blueberries

2 tbsp red grape juice

## Instructions

Preheat the oven to 180°C/350°F/gas mark 4.

Place the fruits in an oven-proof dish, pour the grape juice over them and cover with a well-fitting lid. Cook in the oven for 15-20 minutes then serve immediately.

*Recipe by Carolyn Gibbs*

Vitamin C and cancer-preventing flavonoid antioxidants are the outstanding nutrients found in fruit. Flavonoids also help to keep the walls of blood vessels firm, so that they are less likely to leak water into the spaces between your cells, causing fluid retention.
Like all yellow or orange fruits, peaches and mangos also contain carotenes.
Fresh pineapple is rich in bromelain, an enzyme which can aid digestion by breaking down protein.

# Blueberry and Apple Crispy Pancakes

## Ingredients for 8-10 small pancakes

1 large sweet dessert apple*

115 g/4 ounces/4 tbsp fresh or frozen (defrosted) blueberries or bilberries

55 g/2 ounce chick pea (gram) flour, sieved

25 g/1 ounce ground almonds (almond flour) or ground sesame seeds

75 ml/2¼ fluid oz/5 tbsp apple juice

Groundnut oil

*Choose a variety with plenty of flavour, such as Cox's, Royal Gala, Braeburn or Worcester

## Instructions

Combine the chick pea flour, ground almonds and cinnamon. Slowly add the apple juice, stirring all the time. beat with a wooden spoon until smooth. Grate the apple (including the skin) and add to the batter together with the blueberries. Stir well.

Place a heavy-bottomed frying pan (skillet) over a low to medium heat and add 2 tbsp oil. Once the oil is hot, drop dessertspoons of the batter into the pan, smooth down with a fork, and cook slowly until the bottom of the pancake has browned.

Flip over with a spatula and cook the other side. Re-oil the pan between batches. Serve immediately, with Coconut and Cashew Cream (see page 120) or Banana Crème (see page 113) and garnished with a few slices of fresh fruit such as oranges, pears or mangoes.

*Variation*

Use diced fresh pear and sliced banana instead of blueberries, and crushed or ground cardamom instead of cinnamon.

*Recipe by Carolyn Gibbs*

## What It's Good For

This recipe provides high quality protein from the combination of ground almonds and chick pea flour, super flavonoid-type antioxidants from the skins of the apple and blueberries, and buckets of vitamins and minerals. While it is a common belief that we should not eat anything fried, that belief comes from the confusion that is so rampant about nutrition. It is probably a good idea to stay off deep-fried foods, but we do need to have some oil in our diet; the small amounts used in this book will ensure that you get that oil and are no cause for concern.

# Black Forest Gelled Fruits

## Ingredients for 4 servings

350 g/12 ounces frozen "Black Forest" fruits*

150 ml/5 fluid oz/¾ cup red grape juice measured out, plus extra as required

15 g/½ ounce/1 rounded tbsp powdered gelatine

*E.g. a mixture of blueberries, black cherries, blackberries, black grapes, strawberries, blackcurrants. This type of mixture is sold under various names in large supermarkets. You could also use the equivalent in fresh fruit.

## Instructions

Place the fruit in a saucepan over a medium heat with the lid on and cook for about 3 minutes or until the fruits have softened a little and released some of their juice (if frozen, they do not have to defrost completely).

Remove from the heat. Put the 150 ml grape juice in a small saucepan and bring it to the boil. Take the pan off the heat and sprinkle the gelatine into it, whisking briskly until all the gelatine has dissolved.

Pour the fruit, with its juice, into a measuring jug. Add the dissolved gelatine and then top up with cold red grape juice to the 570 ml/1 pint/2 cup mark. Stir well.

Pour the mixture into a glass dish or mould and refrigerate until set (about two hours). Serve with Coconut and Cashew Cream (see page 120).

*Recipe by Carolyn Gibbs*

## What It's Good For

The berries in this recipe contain a good mix of flavonoids. Flavonoids are the colourful pigments in their skins. The red and blue pigments are known as anthocyanidins. Other flavonoids include catechins (found in grape seeds, cocoa powder and red wine) and quercetin (found in apple skins and onions). The medicinal actions of many herbs and plants (for instance Ginkgo biloba) are now known to be due to their flavonoids. As well as being antioxidants, flavonoids can keep blood vessels healthy and combat inflammation.

# Coconut and Cashew Cream

## Ingredients for 4 servings

1 small tin coconut milk (165 ml/5.6 fluid oz)

85 g/3 ounces/raw cashew nuts, well washed and drained

## Instructions

Warm the coconut milk by putting the unopened can in a small saucepan of hot water for 10 minutes.

Open the can and put the coconut milk and cashews into a blender. Whizz until smooth and creamy, scraping the sides down occasionally with a rubber spatula. This process may take several minutes.

Set aside for one hour to thicken. Warm gently before serving or use cold.

## What It's Good For

Most of us are used to eating salted cashew nuts, and do not realize how deliciously sweet these nuts are in their natural state. Raw cashews are low in oil and rich in potassium and magnesium, iron and zinc. Cashew pieces are often cheaper to buy than whole cashews, but always wash raw cashews before use, as they can develop a little mould, which may affect the flavour as well as being harmful to health. The oils in coconut cream do not have a cholesterol-raising effect. They contain lauric acid, which combats the Epstein-Barr virus.

# Blueberries in Yoghurt Layered with Soft Marzipan and Pear Slices

## Ingredients for 4 servings

175 g/6 ounces fresh or frozen blueberries

1 ripe dessert pear (red-skinned if possible)

225 g/8 ounces plain soya (soy) or sheep's milk yoghurt

55 g/2 ounces ground almonds (almond flour)

55 g/2 ounces dried dates, chopped

4 tbsp red grape juice

Toasted chopped or flaked almonds

## Instructions

Put the chopped dates in a small saucepan over a low heat with 6 tbsp water, cover and cook until soft. Remove from the heat and beat with a wooden spoon to a smooth paste. Stir in the ground almonds. The mixture should be the consistency of thick double cream - add a little more water if necessary.

Put the blueberries in a covered saucepan over a low heat until the juices run. Remove from the heat and leave to cool. Slice the pear thinly and put it in a saucepan over a low heat with the red grape juice to poach gently for 3-4 minutes or until tender. Remove from the heat then remove the pear slices from the pan with a slotted spoon.

Stir the yoghurt, pour it over the cooled blueberries, and fold in gently. Divide the pear slices between four individual glass serving dishes, then pour a layer of date and almond paste over them. Top with the yoghurt and blueberry mixture. Chill in the fridge for at least 1 hour and sprinkle generously with toasted chopped or flaked almonds just before serving.

*Recipe by Carolyn Gibbs*

## What It's Good For

This recipe provides protein from the yoghurt (whichever type is used), flavonoids from the blueberries, and vitamin E, calcium, magnesium and other minerals from the almonds. It is also rich in vitamin C.
See page 28 for the benefits of soya products, and pages 87 and 119 for information on flavonoids.

# Baked Apples Filled with a Soft Cherry Marzipan

## Ingredients for 4 servings

4 large dessert apples, washed and cored

75 g/2½ ounces dried cherries*

75 g/2½ ounces/½ cup ground almonds (almond flour)

2 tbsp toasted flaked almonds

Soya (soy) cream to taste

*Dried cherries and blueberries free of sugar and additives can be found in larger branches of Sainsburys supermarkets. Look in the baking department, near the raisins.

## Instructions

Preheat the oven to 175°C/350°F/Gas mark 4. Put the cherries and just enough water to cover them in a small saucepan over a low heat. Cover and simmer for 10 minutes. Remove from the heat and liquidize the cherries with a hand blender in the pan then mash in the ground almonds.

Using a sharp knife, score a circle around the "waist" of each apple to allow it to expand on cooking, then place the apples in an oiled shallow oven-proof dish and stuff the marzipan into the centre of each apple. Place the dish in the centre of the oven and bake for 45 minutes or until tender. Remove from the oven, cut the apples vertically down the middle then turn them over and slice them thickly, trying not to dislodge the filling. Arrange overlapping apple slices on individual serving plates and serve warm with a topping of soya cream and toasted flaked almonds.

*Variation*

Use dried blueberries, raisins or apricots instead of cherries. Spoon the filling into peach halves instead of apples. Brush with groundnut oil and bake in a very hot oven for 15 minutes.

*Recipe by Linda Lazarides and Carolyn Gibbs*

## What It's Good For

Do not consume marzipan or any nut-rich recipes if you suffer from herpes, since nuts are rich in arginine, an amino acid which can cause flare-ups of the herpes virus. Almonds are rich in calcium and magnesium and are a good source of protein. Apple peel is very rich in cancer-preventing carotenes and flavonoids, as well as pectin. Pectin can help to treat constipation, and it binds to toxins in your intestines and helps your body eliminate them. Try to use organic apples if you can, since any pesticide treatments will be concentrated in the skin.

# Sweet Mango Pudding with Almonds and Cardamom

## Ingredients for 4 servings

300 ml/½ pint/1 cup soya (soy) milk

45 g/1½ ounces/1 rounded tbsp brown rice flour

1 tbsp ground almonds (almond flour)

1 tsp ground cardamom

1 extra-large or two small mangoes

Flaked almonds, toasted

## Instructions

Peel the mango, cut all the flesh off the stone and put it in a bowl. Using a blender or liquidizer, purée the mango flesh until smooth. (If it is not soft enough you can soften it by stewing in a pan for 20 minutes over a low heat with a tablespoon of water.)

Put the soya milk in a saucepan over a medium heat, and whisk the brown rice flour, ground almonds and ground cardamom into it. Bring to the boil, stirring, then turn the heat down low and continue stirring for another 6 minutes to thicken.

Remove from the heat, then stir the mango purée into the contents of the saucepan. Beat well until smooth and uniform.

Pour the pudding into individual glass dishes. Pour a little soya cream on top and swirl it. Can also be served cold, garnished with toasted almonds and some finely diced dried fruit such as dates or unsulphured apricots.

## What It's Good For

Like brown rice, brown rice flour is a good source of B vitamins and also methionine, a protein constituent (amino acid) which your liver needs to make an important antioxidant enzyme. Mangoes are a good source of vitamin C and carotenes—antioxidants related to the beta carotene in carrots. Mangoes also contain flavonoids (more about these on pages 87 and 119).

# Melon Balls in Ginger and Orange Sauce

## Ingredients for 2 servings

1 chilled cantaloupe melon large
   enough to serve 2 people

275 ml/½ pint/1 cup orange juice*
   (freshly squeezed if possible)

1 tbsp shredded orange zest

1 rounded tsp arrowroot powder

1 tsp finely grated fresh ginger

*If you can get ruby red oranges, this makes a
lovely colour contrast with the melon.

## Instructions

Put one tbsp of the orange juice into a small bowl with the arrowroot powder and the rest in a saucepan over a medium heat. Stir the arrowroot powder and juice together until smooth, then add to the saucepan along with the ginger and zest. Stir until the mixture just begins to simmer then immediately remove from the heat.

Allow the sauce to cool.

Using a melon baller, make as many balls as you can from the melon. Place in individual serving dishes and spoon the sauce over them.

## What It's Good For

Orange zest is rich in flavonoid antioxidants (see pages 87 and 119). Orange juice, especially if very fresh, is a good source of the B vitamin folic acid as well as vitamin C and carotenes antioxidants (related to beta carotene in carrots. Folic acid is often in short supply in diets which rely on convenience food, because it is very vulnerable to heat and light.
Ginger is a great aid to the digestion and helps to stimulate the circulation.

# Yoghurt Cheesecake with Black Forest Fruits

**Makes one 8 inch diameter cake**

*For the base*

80 g/3 ounces/fine oatmeal

55 g/2 ounces raisins

55 g/2 ounces coconut oil, chilled

25 g/1 ounce spelt flour

*For the topping*

225 g/8 ounces frozen "Black Forest" fruits

450 g/1 pound/2 cups sheep's yoghurt

15 g/½ ounce gelatine powder

1 tsp natural vanilla extract

Red grape juice as required

*e.g. a mixture of blueberries, black cherries, blackberries, black grapes, strawberries, blackcurrants. This type of mixture is sold under different names in large supermarkets. You could also use the equivalent in fresh fruit.

**Instructions**

Preheat the oven to gas mark 5. Put the oatmeal, spelt flour and raisins in a food processor with the S blade, and process until the raisins are finely chopped and blended with the flours. Transfer to a bowl, add the vanilla extract and solid coconut oil and mash into the flour with a fork until the mixture resembles fine breadcrumbs. Press it evenly on to the base of an oiled 8-inch diameter foil pie dish or sandwich tin (not one with a removable bottom). Bake for 10-15 minutes until golden then allow to cool.

Pour the yoghurt into a sieve lined with absorbent kitchen paper suspended over a bowl and leave it to drip for at least one hour.

Put the fruits in a covered saucepan over a low heat to cook gently in their own steam. Once they have released their juices, purée them in the pan with a hand blender. Bring the purée to the boil, then remove from the heat and sprinkle in the gelatine. Whisk briskly until it dissolves.

Combine strained yoghurt and fruit purée in a measuring jug. If the contents do not reach the 1 pint mark, top up with red grape juice. Whizz again with the blender until smooth, then pour into the sandwich tin over the pastry base and refrigerate until set.

# Chocolate Mousse

## Ingredients for 3 servings

250 g/9 ounces firm silken tofu

55 g/2 ounces dried dates

2 heaped tbsp cocoa powder

1 tsp natural vanilla extract

Soya (soy) milk as required

Soya (soy) cream and grated bitter chocolate to garnish

## Instructions

Put the dates in a small saucepan and add just enough water to cover them. Cover, bring to the boil and simmer for 15 minutes or until soft.

Remove the dates with a slotted spoon (keep the cooking liquid) and put them in a food processor with the remaining ingredients. Whizz for half a minute, then scrape the sides down with a rubber spatula and check the thickness of the mixture. The firmer the tofu you have used, the more liquid it will need, so keep adding the date cooking liquid until you have a soft dropping consistency. If it still needs more liquid, add a little soya milk.

Keep whizzing until the texture is completely smooth and creamy. (This may take a few minutes).

Serve in glass dishes, decorated with a little soya cream and grated bitter chocolate.

*Variations*

For fruity mousses, use equal weights of silken tofu and all-fruit jam or spread (such as apricot). Thin with a little soya milk if necessary, and flavour with natural vanilla extract.

## What It's Good For

Chocaholics will love this recipe. They won't realize that this mousse is made with protein from health-giving soya instead of the fats which can make overindulgence in ordinary chocolate so harmful. Cocoa powder is rich in iron and magnesium, and even in antioxidant flavonoids too. But do not use it if you suffer from breast lumps or cysts or any form of breast tenderness. Cocoa and chocolate contain caffeine-like compounds which seem to encourage breast problems in some women. Dates are a great source of dietary fibre.

# Miscellaneous

Recipes for pastry, mayonnaise, ketchup, unleavened bread, apple sauce, and other useful extras.

# Sour Cream

## Ingredients for 6 servings

250 g/9 ounces silken tofu*

2 tbsp apple juice

Up to 6 tbsp water

4 tbsp cold-pressed unrefined sunflower oil

2 tbsp fresh lemon juice

½ tsp natural vanilla extract

*Silken tofu has a creamy blancmange-like texture. It comes in soft, medium and firm varieties. The firmer the tofu, the more water you will need to blend into it for this recipe.

## Instructions

Whizz all the ingredients except the water in a blender. If it is too thick, whizz in the water little by little until you reach the desired consistency. For savoury recipes you might also want to add a pinch of potassium salt.

*Variations*

### Garlic Sour Cream

Add half a clove of chopped raw garlic and a pinch of potassium salt to the other ingredients in the blender before whizzing.

### Mustard Sour Cream

Add a teaspoon of mustard powder to the other ingredients in the blender before whizzing.

## What It's Good For

It is not widely known that the taste of cow's milk comes from a combination of lactose (milk sugar) and coumarin, a flavonoid-like substance found in hay and clover. Coumarin has a flavour almost identical to vanilla, which is why a little vanilla extract is used in this recipe. See page 28 for the benefits of consuming soya products.

# Garlic Crème

**Makes 300 ml/½ pint/1 cup garlic crème**

50 g/1¾ ounces/½ cup soya (soy) flour

275 ml/½ pint/1 cup boiling water

100 ml/3 fluid oz/⅓ cup cold-pressed unrefined sunflower oil*

1 tbsp flax seed oil (optional)

1 tbsp lemon juice

1 clove fresh garlic, roughly chopped

½ tsp potassium salt

*Can be replaced with extra virgin olive oil if you are a candidiasis sufferer.

## Instructions

The flavours of soya and garlic complement each other perfectly in this delicious recipe, which is one of the best medicinal foods in this book.

Add the soya flour to the boiling water in a saucepan, and whisk to ensure no lumps remain. Simmer gently for 20 minutes, stirring from time to time and ensure it does not boil over. Remove from the heat and allow to cool.

Transfer to the goblet of a liquidiser and whizz with the lemon juice, salt, garlic and half the main oil. When smooth add the rest of the oil plus the flax seed oil (if you are using it) and whizz again for 1-2 minutes. This Garlic Crème will keep for a few days in the fridge, and you can also stir in other flavourings such as chopped herbs or mustard. Stir before use. Use cold as a topping or a dressing or as a sauce with fish.

## What It's Good For

Raw garlic contains allicin, which is destroyed by cooking but has many health benefits. Once you have eaten it, allicin travels to all parts of the body and sterilizes your lungs. That's good news for bronchitis sufferers. Raw garlic has been used to treat dysentery, typhoid, cholera, bacterial food poisoning and worms, as well as intestinal infections such as cryptosporidial diarrhoea associated with immune deficiency and AIDS. It can also help to heal the bowels after amoebic dysentery and to combat the thrush-causing yeast *Candida albicans*. Flax seed oil is one of the few good sources of the essential polyunsaturated fatty acids known as alpha linolenic acid.

# Apple Sauce and Apple Butter

**Makes 570 ml/1 pint/2 cups apple sauce plus 275 ml/½ pint/1 cup of apple butter**

2 kg/4½ pounds sweet apples with a good flavour, such as Cox's

150 ml/¼ pint/½ cup water

**Special Equipment**

A pressure cooker

## Instructions

Core and segment the apples (this task is very quick if you use a coring/segmenting gadget) but do not peel them. Put the segments in a pressure cooker with the water, bring up to full steam and cook for 10 minutes.

Cool the pressure cooker and remove the lid. Put the contents in a food processor (with the S blade) and whizz until smooth. You will probably need to do this in two batches. It takes a few minutes to really pulverize the peel.

Return the apple purée to the pan, and leave over a medium heat for one hour, stirring from time to time. Turn the heat down to prevent violent sputtering. At the end of this time, use a ladle to spoon out 570 ml/1 pint/2 cups of the purée, which you can now use as apple sauce, and leave the rest to continue reducing over the heat for another 3 hours. At the end of this time you should have a very thick mixture which stiffens on cooling and becomes spreadable like butter.

Both apple sauce and apple butter can be frozen. You could freeze them in ice cube trays if you will only need to defrost a small amount at a time.

## What It's Good For

Apple peel contains amazing nutritional value. It is very rich in cancer-preventing carotenes and flavonoids, as well as a type of soluble dietary fibre known as pectin. Pectin is a gelling agent used in jam making, and is the reason why this apple sauce recipe can thicken soya milk and turn it into custard (see page 114). Pectin can also help to treat constipation, and it binds to toxins in your intestines and helps your body eliminate them. The skin is the most nutritious part of the apple, but is also the part most liable to contain concentrated pesticides, alar (a chemical ripening agent), and pesticide-treated wax, so make this recipe with organic apples if you can.

# Basic Tomato Sauce

## Ingredients for 2 servings

2 cans chopped Italian plum
    tomatoes

3 cloves garlic, finely chopped

A few pieces dried porcini
    mushrooms, chopped small

1 tbsp capers, chopped

1 tbsp coriander (cilantro) chopped

2 tbsp extra virgin olive oil

Potassium salt

Freshly ground black pepper

## Instructions

Put all the ingredients except the black pepper into a saucepan, bring to the boil, then simmer for one hour with the lid off or until reduced to a thick, glossy consistency. Stir in freshly-ground black pepper. This sauce can be served with wheat-free pasta, rösti recipes or grilled fish.

## What It's Good For

Tomato sauce is very rich in a carotene known as lycopene, which is especially powerful in preventing prostate cancer and is thought to be an even stronger neutraliser of free radicals than beta carotene. This concentrated sauce is also an excellent source of potassium, vitamin C and minerals.

# Mayonnaise

**Makes about 300 ml/½ pint/1 cup**

<u>100 g/3½ ounces silken tofu*</u>

<u>1 tbsp fresh lemon juice</u>

<u>100 ml/3½ fluid oz mild-flavoured extra virgin olive oil</u>

<u>Up to 100 ml/3½ fluid oz water</u>

<u>Potassium salt</u>

*If you are using a soft silken tofu, you will need only a fraction of the water. If you are using an extra-firm silken tofu such as Sanchi Organic Tofu, you will need all of it.

## Instructions

Using a blender, liquidise the tofu with the lemon juice, some or all of the water (depending on the softness of the tofu) and the potassium salt, then whizz in the olive oil.

This makes a thick basic mayonnaise. It can easily be thinned by whizzing in more water, or stretched by whizzing in more oil.

### Variations

Mayonnaise can be flavoured with a teaspoon of pale miso (see page 24) which has been whisked into hot water and then allowed to cool, or with garlic, mustard, horseradish or spring onion (scallion) among others.

## What It's Good For

Tofu (made from soya) is a rich source of hormone-balancing flavonoids known as isoflavones, which help to prevent problems relating to excess of insufficient oestrogen, and excess testosterone—a male hormone related to oestrogen. So a diet rich in tofu can help to prevent all kinds of problems, from menopausal hot flushes, to breast cancer and prostate cancer. Extra virgin olive oil is an important part of the Mediterranean diet, which helps prevent health problems in old age and is also now known to help prevent a deterioration of mental faculties.

# Short Crust Pastry

**When rolled out makes 2 pastry rounds with a diameter of about 25 cm/10 inches.**

100 g/3½ ounces/scant 1 cup brown rice flour

100 g/3½ ounces/scant 1 cup spelt flour[1]

100 g/3½ ounces/scant 1 cup solid coconut oil[2], chilled

120 ml/4 fluid ounces/scant ½ cup water

1. See page 26
2. See page 23

## Instructions

Preheat the oven to 190°C/375°F gas mark 5.

Sift the dry ingredients into a large bowl, then add the solid coconut oil. Using a fork, mash the oil into the flours until the mixture resembles fine breadcrumbs. Add the water little by little, working it into the mixture with a rubber spatula until you can form a large, soft ball of dough with your hands. Knead briefly then refrigerate for at least half an hour.

Oil the tin (metal produces the best results) which will be in contact with the pastry while cooking. Remove the dough from the fridge, and knead only until you can roll the pastry out without it breaking up. If you find it hard to roll then you have not added enough water; try to work a little more water into the dough.

Roll out the pastry evenly, using brown rice flour to prevent it sticking, and turning it 90 degrees from time to time. Then use this pastry as you would any other shortcrust pastry: to make pasties, pies, pastry cases for flans, and so on. Bake for about 20 minutes or until golden.

If baking blind, prick the base with a fork before baking, to prevent air bubbles.

## What It's Good For

This makes a very respectable shortcrust pastry with a good, light texture. The coconut oil should not make this pastry taste of coconut. Although solid at room temperature and so technically speaking a hard or saturated fat, the European Journal of Clinical Nutrition reports that consuming coconut oil does not causes increases in blood cholesterol levels. In fact coconut oil could be especially beneficial to people with chronic fatigue syndrome since the monolauric acid it contains can combat "lipid-coated" viruses such as Epstein-Barr.

# Unleavened Bread

## Ingredients for approx 9 x 6-inch wide rounds of bread

10 oz/275 g wholemeal spelt flour*

2 tbsp thick soya (soy) yoghurt

100 ml/3½ fluid oz/scant ½ cup water

*See page 26

## Instructions

Add the yoghurt and water to the flour and mix to a soft, pliable dough. Turn out on to a well-floured board and knead for about 8 minutes until the dough is smooth and elastic, using more flour if necessary to prevent sticking. Put in a bowl covered with a damp cloth for 30 minutes.

Break off egg-sized pieces of dough, and roll into rounds measuring about 6 inches in diameter and ¼ inch thick. Preheat an unoiled griddle pan or good quality frying pan (skillet) on a moderate heat for about 2 minutes. When the pan is hot, place a round of dough on it and cook for about a minute until the bread puffs up slightly. Briefly dab it all over very gently with a spatula to make it puff up more. Then immediately turn it over and repeat this on the other side. Turn and cook the other side. When both sides are cooked, turn the bread over again and .

Stack the rounds separated by absorbent kitchen paper. Keep warm until you are ready to serve them.

*To Freeze*

Slightly undercook the breads and omit the puffing up stage. Allow to cool, place them in polythene freezer bags and then in the freezer. To use, finish cooking the breads under a hot grill (broiler), but not too close to the heat as they will puff up.

## What It's Good For

Spelt flour is a variety of wheat (sometimes known as "ancient wheat"), but does not cause problems for people with a wheat intolerance.
It has all the nutritional benefits of wholemeal flour: B vitamins, vitamin E and minerals.
But cooked in this way, without yeast, wholemeal spelt and wheat (and bran products made from them) can contain high levels of phytic acid, a substance which binds to minerals in your diet and prevents you from absorbing them. This should not be a problem if your diet is varied and you eat this bread only in moderate amounts.

# Pan-Baked Pea Bread

## Ingredients for 8 thin rounds about 4 inches wide

200g/7 ounces/1 cup chick pea (gram) flour

100 ml/3½ fluid oz/scant ½ cup water

2 tbsp arrowroot powder

1 tbsp groundnut oil

Brown rice flour for rolling out

Potassium salt

## Instructions

Mix the dry ingredients then add the water and oil, and mix thoroughly, using the back of a spoon to work the ingredients together into a thick, stiff and sticky dough.

Divide the dough into 8 portions. Using brown rice flour to prevent sticking, roll the mixture into balls and flatten with your hand. Then, using a rolling pin, roll into thin rounds.

Preheat a dry griddle pan or good quality frying pan (skillet) over a medium heat until very hot. Put a dough round in the pan and cook for about one minute or until it puffs up and small brown spots appear on the bottom. Turn and cook the other side. These light and tasty breads are delicious served warm with soup, and can also be folded over and stuffed with salad ingredients plus any of the following:

- Grated hard goat's cheese,
- One of the Speciality Patés (pages 44-46),
- Guacamole (page 52),
- Hummus (page 41).

## What It's Good For

Gram (chick pea) flour is very rich in protein. It is also a good source of many other nutrients, including calcium, magnesium, iron, copper and some of the B vitamins.

# Cacik (yoghurt and cucumber sauce)

**Ingredients for 4 servings**

One standard tub of sheep's
yoghurt (about 250 grams, or
half a pint/1 cup in volume)

Half a cucumber, finely shredded or
coarsely grated

1 clove garlic, crushed

2 tsp fresh mint, finely chopped, or
1 tsp dried mint

Potassium salt

Freshly ground black pepper

**Instructions**

Combine the ingredients and mix well. Use as a dip or as a sauce for Falafels (see page 54) or Spiced Bean Röstis (see page 48).

Sheep's yoghurt, while rich in protein like cow's milk yoghurt, is usually safe to eat for people who have a cow's milk allergy. Yoghurt is also rich in beneficial bacteria for the intestines. Cucumber is rich in potassium and other minerals, and is a particularly good source of bone- and tissue-building silica. But do not peel your cucumbers, as these nutrients are mostly concentrated in the skin. Mint is used by herbalists as a remedy to help the digestion and soothe inflammation in the intestines.

# Home-Made Tomato Ketchup

**Makes 225 ml/8 fluid oz/¾ cup**

1 small can of tomato purée (paste)
    (140 g/5 ounces)

3 tbsp cider vinegar or wine
    vinegar

3 tbsp water

½ tsp English mustard powder

Freshly ground nutmeg

Potassium salt

Freshly ground black pepper

**Instructions**

Mix the ingredients thoroughly and store in a jar in the fridge for up to four days.

*Variations*

Spice the ketchup up with cayenne pepper or some chopped gherkins or capers.

## What It's Good For

No artificial preservatives, colourings or flavourings, no sugar or salt, this is quick to make but better than any commercial brand. Tomato purée is very rich in a carotene known as lycopene, which is especially powerful in preventing prostate cancer and is thought to be an even stronger neutralizer of free radicals than beta carotene.

# Sweet Chestnut Crust

**When rolled out makes 2 x pastry rounds with a diameter of about 25 cm/10 inches.**

100 g/3½ ounces/scant 1 cup chestnut flour[1]

100 g/3½ ounces/scant 1 cup spelt flour[2]

100 g/3½ ounces/scant 1 cup solid coconut oil, chilled

120 ml/4 fluid ounces/scant ½ cup white grape juice

20 g/¾ ounce soya (soy) milk powder[3]

½ tsp potassium baking powder

1. See page 23.

2. See page 26.

3. Available from health food shops.

## Instructions

Preheat the oven to 190°C/375°F gas mark 5.

Sift the dry ingredients into a large bowl, then add the coconut oil, which should be in solid form. Using a fork, mash the oil into the dry ingredients until the mixture resembles fine breadcrumbs. Add the grape juice little by little, working it into the mixture with a rubber spatula until you can form a large, soft ball of dough with your hands. Knead briefly then refrigerate for at least half an hour.

Oil the tin (metal produces the best results) which will be in contact with the pastry while cooking. Remove the dough from the fridge, and knead only until you can roll the pastry out without it breaking up. If you find it hard to roll then you have not added enough liquid; try to work a little more grape juice into the dough.

Roll out the pastry evenly, using extra spelt flour to prevent it sticking, and turning it 90 degrees from time to time. Then use this pastry to make cases for sweet desserts, tarts and tartlets. Bake for about 25 minutes or until golden. To prevent air bubbles prick the base with a fork before baking blind.

## What It's Good For

The main benefits of this recipe come from the chestnut flour, rich in potassium, magnesium and iron, and spelt flour, rich in B vitamins and vitamin E. Although solid at room temperature, coconut oil does not seem to raise cholesterol levels like butter and other animal fats. It contains beneficial plant sterols, which help to prevent cholesterol rises. It also contains lauric acid, which combats the Epstein-Barr virus, known to be the cause of many cases of chronic fatigue syndrome.

# Drinks

**R**ecipes for teas to help your digestion, and nutrient-packed juices to combat arthritis and other problems and to help your liver.

# Digestive Tea

## Ingredients for 2 cup/mugfuls

600 ml/1 pint/2 cups very hot water

1 tsp fresh ginger, grated (or ½ tsp ground ginger)

1 tsp fennel seeds

½ tsp ground cinnamon

¼ tsp ground cloves

## Instructions

Using a mortar and pestle, crush the fennel seeds and mix with the other spices. Put the mixture in a small teapot and pour the boiling water over it. Stir thoroughly, cover and leave for 5 minutes, then strain through a very fine strainer and drink.

## What It's Good For

These spices are prescribed by medical herbalists to soothe the digestion after a meal and to treat flatulence. If you are not used to eating the foods in this book and have any trouble digesting them, this tea will be a great help while your body is adapting. Sip it slowly after your meal. If you'd like it to be even more effective, you could also add a pinch of cayenne pepper, but watch out for the extra bite!

# Home-Made Apple, Celery, Parsley And Radish Juice

## Ingredients for 1 serving

1 large sweet apple, unpeeled and organically grown if possible

2 sticks celery

1 bunch parsley

5 cm/2 inch segment of mooli radish

Small piece of lemon, including peel*

*Optional - you may find that it helps the flavour

## Special Equipment

A juice extractor

## Instructions

Wash the ingredients, cut them into chunks and put them through a juice extractor. Stir and leave to stand for 20 minutes to break down the peppery taste of the radish before drinking.

## What It's Good For

It would be hard to find a drink more rich in health-giving nutrients. This drink is:

Rich in vitamin C.

Helps your liver and gall bladder to remove pollutants from your body.

Helps to alkalinize your body.

Fights fluid retention, which causes pain and swellings in nerves, joints and breasts, as well as migraine and headaches.

Helps fight arthritis.

# Beetroot, Celery And Lemon Juice

**Prepare quantities of ingredients according to how many people you are catering for**

<u>Bottled beetroot (beet) juice (or juice from raw beetroot made with a juice extractor)</u>

<u>Home-made celery juice</u>

<u>Fresh lemon juice</u>

**Special Equipment**

A juice extractor

**Instructions**

Combine equal quantities of bottled beetroot juice and home-made celery juice made from fresh celery with a juice extractor, or use the proportions you prefer. Flavour with a little fresh lemon juice to taste.

If you juice your own raw beetroot, it will be very strong and only a little is required. It must be left to stand for 20 minutes before drinking or else it will have a very peppery taste.

**What It's Good For**

Beetroot juice is a powerful aid to your liver and gall bladder. It helps stimulate them to drain and release their contents. This ensures that processed toxins are removed from your body as quickly as possible, provided that your bowels are working efficiently. Celery juice helps to alkalinize the body, thus combating the acidity that often leads to arthritis. It also contains coumarin, a substance which fights fluid retention by keeping your blood vessels strong and stimulating your lymphatic system. Fluid retention can simulate arthritis by pressing on joints and causing pain and swelling.

# Home-Made Broccoli Stem And Sharp Apple Juice

**Prepare quantities of ingredients according to how many people you are catering for**

Equal quantities of

Broccoli stems

Sharp apples such as Granny Smiths

**Instructions**

Broccoli juice is very sweet, which is why it is good mixed with a fairly sharp apple juice. Simply cut the broccoli stems and apples into chunks and feed into your juice extractor in the proportions you prefer. You may need to experiment a little. If necessary, add a little lemon juice to disguise the broccoli flavour.

**Special Equipment**

A juice extractor

## What It's Good For

Save your broccoli heads for eating and the thick stems for juicing, especially if you have any female troubles linked to poor oestrogen metabolism, such as: Breast cysts or lumps Endometriosis Fibroids Family history of breast cancer. Broccoli contains substances which help your liver to break down excess oestradiol, the form of oestrogen which in excess can encourage these problems. Broccoli juice also helps your liver break down many other potentially harmful substances. It is a superb liver food.

# Carrot And Orange Juice

**Prepare quantities of ingredients according to how many people you are catering for**

<u>Carrots</u>

<u>Fresh oranges</u>

Try to get organic oranges, or at least unwaxed ones. If you cannot obtain them, scrub ordinary oranges carefully in very hot water with detergent to remove the thin layer of pesticide-treated wax coating the skin, and then rinse.

**Special Equipment**

<u>A juice extractor</u>

**Instructions**

This is a lovely sweet combination. Juice your carrots in the juice-extractor together with some of the orange flesh and peel. Then juice the rest of the orange with a normal citrus juicer.

Mix together in the proportions you prefer and drink straight away.

If you do not have a juice extractor, use commercial juices and use your liquidizer to whizz in a piece of orange with the pith and peel still attached.

## What It's Good For

Carrots are rich in beta carotene and other carotenes (a type of antioxidant) as well as in many minerals. Beta carotene can also be converted into vitamin A, although if you have an underactive thyroid this process may not be as efficient as it should be. Any beta carotene that your body cannot handle is stored in your skin, turning you yellowy-orange!
Fresh oranges are rich in the important B vitamin folic acid. The pith and peel is an excellent source of a type of antioxidant known as flavonoids, which can fight fluid retention.

# Flavonoid-Rich Orange Juice

## Ingredients

<u>Ready-made orange juice, plus</u>

<u>Fresh oranges</u>

Try to get organic oranges, or at least unwaxed ones. If you cannot obtain them, scrub ordinary oranges carefully in very hot water with detergent to remove the thin layer of pesticide-treated wax coating the skin, and then rinse.

## Instructions

Liquidize a piece of fresh orange with pith and peel into a glass of normal orange juice. This will contain a far larger quantity of flavonoids than you could get in a flavonoid supplement pill!

## What It's Good For

As mentioned on page 144, fresh orange juice is rich in folic acid, one of the nutrients most likely to be in short supply in our diet. It is now known that one of the biggest causes of the high blood cholesterol levels that lead to heart attacks is a folic acid deficiency, which can be detected by measuring levels of a substance known as homocysteine in your blood. People with high homocysteine levels are at the highest risk of heart attacks, and these homocysteine levels can often be brought down by increasing the amount of folic acid (and sometimes also vitamins B6 and B12) in your diet.

# Home-Made Ginger Tea With Lemon Zest

### Ingredients to make one cup or mugful

One tsp fresh grated ginger

One tsp fresh, finely shredded
lemon zest*

*Try to get organic lemons, or at
least unwaxed ones. If you cannot
obtain them, scrub ordinary lemons
carefully in very hot water with
detergent to remove the thin layer
of pesticide-treated wax coating
the skin, and then rinse.

### Instructions

Pour a cupful of boiling water on to a teaspoon of
grated fresh ginger and a teaspoon of fresh lemon zest
shreds. Leave to infuse for five minutes, then strain
and drink.

## What It's Good For

Ginger is known as a "hot
bitter" herb, which helps
your stomach to produce
digestive juices and
therefore aids digestion.
It is a useful herb for many
stomach problems, and
much research has been
carried out into its
benefits, especially against
rheumatoid arthritis and
travel sickness.
In Chinese medicine,
ginger is considered to be
a warming stimulant to the
circulation and to remove
catarrh and help bronchitic
conditions.
Lemon zest is rich in
flavonoids, anti-cancer
antioxidants which also
help the circulation by
keeping blood vessels
strong and healthy.

# Almond Milk

## Ingredients for 2 servings

570 ml/1 pint/2 cups water

55 g/2 ounces/scant ½ cup
chopped almonds*

*Can be made by whizzing blanched almonds in
a food processor

## Instructions

Soak the chopped almonds in the water overnight in the goblet of your liquidizer.

In the morning whizz them together until the almonds have turned into a fine pulp, and strain the milk through a fine sieve.

This delicious milk is naturally sweet and excellent for drinking. The pulp can be added to rice pudding.

Try the same method with other nuts or seeds, such as brazils, cashews and sunflower seeds.

## What It's Good For

While not as rich in protein as cow's milk, soya milk and nut milks do contain a good range of nutrients, especially calcium and magnesium, essential polyunsaturated oils, zinc and vitamin E. But if you have a young baby these alternative milks are not a suitable substitute for formula milks. All young children must have the right balance of protein, fats and oils to help them grow. Although almonds are calorie-rich (about 600 Calories per 100 grams) feeding nut milk too early, before the baby's digestion has matured, could result in developing an allergy.

# Soda Pop

## Ingredients

<u>Equal quantities of sparkling mineral water and any combination of:</u>

<u>Red or white grape juice</u>

<u>Apple juice</u>

<u>Orange juice</u>

<u>Mango, passion fruit, peach, pineapple or raspberry juices</u>

Use either ready-made juices or make your own with a juice extractor

## Instructions

Just mix your favourite combinations together and drink immediately. Try for some interesting colours such as mixing raspberry and orange juice.

You could also liquidize small amounts of soft fruit into the juice before mixing it with the mineral water.

## What It's Good For

These drinks are especially good for hyperactive children, who often react badly to the colourings and sugar in canned fizzy drinks. These commercial drinks can also contain large amounts of phosphorus. Although we all need phosphorus, if it gets out of balance with the other minerals in our bodies it can start to leach calcium from our bones, encouraging bone softness and osteoporosis (brittle bone disease).

It goes without saying that fresh fruit juices are also rich in vitamin C and flavonoid and carotene antioxidants.

# Appendix I
# Nutritional Self-Help

Of all natural therapies, the one most suitable for self-help is nutritional therapy.

Your body is made from millions of small cells. These cells are very similar to plants: they need little more than nutrients, water and oxygen, and a warm, relatively toxin-free environment. If a plant in your house becomes ill, your first instinct is to consider potential stressors: parasites, soil quality, water levels and so on. And of course different plants suffer from different stressors.

Nutritional therapists use the same kind of basic, common-sense approach to treating human ill-health. Eating a faulty diet is of course a big stressor. But problems with any one part of your body can also stress any other part, so if your liver is overloaded, waste products and pollutants can build up and interfere with your internal chemistry. If your digestion is not good, undigested food can encourage food intolerances and toxin-producing bacteria in your intestines.

Let's take a look at some common health problems, the stressors which contribute to them, and some suggestions for nutritional techniques that you can apply to combat them. If you have any difficulty with this, don't give up—it could just be that you need expert advice from a nutritional therapist (see page 162).

## ARTHRITIS

Osteoarthritis is said to affect about 90 per cent of people over the age of 70, so don't be put off by reassurances that it is hereditary. For most people it is curable by nutritional means.

Some of the leading causes of osteoarthritis are:

- Food intolerances.

- Too much acidity in the body from consuming too much protein.

- A deficiency of essential polyunsaturated oils.

- Long-term fluid retention around the joints, which encourages degeneration of the joints.

- An overloaded liver, often made worse by long-term constipation.

So to treat this condition, you would benefit from:

- Finding out whether you have any food intolerances by carrying out the test on pages 156-157.

- Regularly using the recipes in this book, which are mostly not high in protein, and provide the right oils.

- Following the Liver Rejuvenation Programme on pages

158-159.

- Regular massage of the affected areas, imagining that you are stroking excess fluid towards the centre of your body.

- You may also find great relief from taking supplements of evening primrose oil, especially if alcohol seems to aggravate your arthritis.

## ASTHMA

Asthma attacks occur when the bronchial tubes go into spasm due to histamine, a substance associated with allergic symptoms such as swellings and itching. Factors which contribute to asthma include:

- Allergies to inhaled matter such as dust mite droppings,

- Food intolerances,

- Magnesium and B vitamin deficiency,

- Excess salt consumption,

- Liver overload.

So it's worth carrying out the Food Intolerance Test and the Liver Rejuvenation Programme (pages 156-159). Use the recipes in this book as regularly as you can: they are rich in vitamins and minerals and very low in salt. Research suggests that taking strong magnesium and vitamin B6 supplements (follow the directions on the product label) could speed up your progress.

## CANCER PREVENTION

Medical science is now 100 per cent behind the strategy of preventing cancer by eating more fruit and vegetables, which contain the antioxidant vitamins and minerals, the carotenes and flavonoids which help to prevent normal cells from becoming damaged and cancerous.

Cancers are also said to be a problem of the immune system, since it is normally responsible for destroying abnormal cells. Many factors, including emotional ones, faulty nutrition and an overloaded liver can weaken the immune system.

Using the recipes in this book will give you the best possible nutritional protection. Some nutrients are also highly protective against specific cancers, so you should eat soya (soy) foods, broccoli and other members of the cabbage family to prevent breast cancer, tomato sauce to prevent prostate cancer and wholegrains (rich in dietary fibre) to prevent colon cancer. It goes without saying that if you smoke, you should give up as soon as possible. Even the best diet cannot fully protect a smoker from lung cancer.

## CANDIDIASIS

This is a type of *dysbiosis*—a condition where the intestines become overgrown with the wrong type of bacteria or yeasts and fungi (in this case the yeast *Candida albicans*). These micro-organisms produce toxic substances which irritate the intestines and are absorbed into the bloodstream. In large amounts they can be particularly stressful to the liver.

The diagram opposite shows how dysbiosis occurs, often starting with bad digestion, irritation and inflammation of the intestine. Yeasts such as *Candida albicans* are especially encouraged by antibiotics and by sugar consumption.

You would benefit from the Intestinal Healing Programme on page 160-161.

## CHRONIC FATIGUE

When leading a normal life leaves you feeling exhausted, you are said to suffer from chronic, or persistent fatigue. Often, sleep does not refresh you. If they are able to get out of the house at all, chronic fatigue sufferers may go to bed straight after getting home from work. Many people with this problem are bed-bound. Symptoms that can accompany it include muscle pain and "brain fag" - a frightening loss of the ability to concentrate on anything and to get your head round any but the simplest thoughts.

Causes of chronic fatigue include

- The lingering effects of viruses such as the Epstein-Barr virus which causes glandular fever (infectious mononucleosis),

- Sensitivity to chemicals,

- Nutritional deficiencies,

- Food intolerances,

- Dysbiosis: a toxic condition of the intestines which

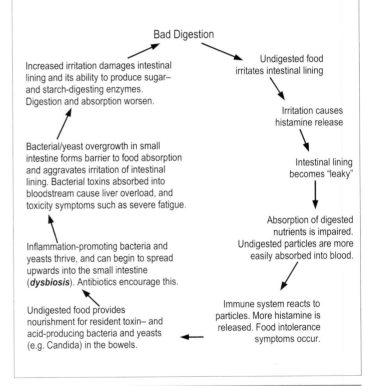

# THE VICIOUS CIRCLE OF DYSBIOSIS

Bad Digestion

Undigested food irritates intestinal lining

Irritation causes histamine release

Intestinal lining becomes "leaky"

Absorption of digested nutrients is impaired. Undigested particles are more easily absorbed into blood.

Immune system reacts to particles. More histamine is released. Food intolerance symptoms occur.

Undigested food provides nourishment for resident toxin– and acid-producing bacteria and yeasts (e.g. Candida) in the bowels.

Inflammation-promoting bacteria and yeasts thrive, and can begin to spread upwards into the small intestine (*dysbiosis*). Antibiotics encourage this.

Bacterial/yeast overgrowth in small intestine forms barrier to food absorption and aggravates irritation of intestinal lining. Bacterial toxins absorbed into bloodstream cause liver overload, and toxicity symptoms such as severe fatigue.

Increased irritation damages intestinal lining and its ability to produce sugar– and starch-digesting enzymes. Digestion and absorption worsen.

overloads the liver and is often brought on by taking anti-biotics (see diagram on page 151).

The first step in treating this problem is to follow the Food In-tolerance Test instructions on page 156-157. This will show you which of your symptoms are caused by a food intoler-ance and which are not. Most people with chronic fatigue would also benefit from the Liver Rejuvenation Programme on page 158-159, which helps to treat chemical sensitivity, and the Intestinal Healing Programme on page 160-161, which treats dysbiosis.

If all these measures do not bring about a considerable improvement in six months or less, then it is possible that you have an active virus which has evaded detection by your doc-tors. If the virus is of the "lipid-coated" type it may be possible to combat it by using coconut oil in your cooking. Such vi-ruses are sensitive to a substance known as lauric acid found in coconut oil.

## PREVENTING GALL-STONES

By middle age, many people (usually women) are admitted into hospital to have their gall bladder removed owing to gall-stones. Now known to be mostly due to a faulty diet contain-ing too much sugar and fat, and too few wholemeal foods, gall-stones are usually an entirely preventable condition. This cookbook is ideal to help keep your gall bladder healthy. By storing bile needed for your digestion, your gall bladder helps you to break down your food properly and so to avoid devel-oping nutritional deficiencies.

## PREVENTING HEART ATTACKS, STROKES, HIGH BLOOD PRES-SURE AND HIGH CHOLESTEROL

If you are using this book because either you or someone in your family is at risk of, or suffers from, any of these prob-lems, you can feel reassured that medical science fully sup-ports the effectiveness of nutritional therapy in combating them. No drug or medicine could possibly do what these reci-pes can do for you, but remember that it's not enough just to use them occasionally. The more you use this book, the bet-ter your protection will be.

Causes of heart attacks, strokes and high blood pressure in-clude:

- Eating a diet providing inadequate amounts of vitamins and minerals. This happens when your normal diet is high in convenience foods, fried, fatty or sugary foods, red meat and alcohol.

- Eating too much saturated fat, which makes your blood sticky, and so prone to forming tiny clots in small blood vessels.

- Not eating enough fresh vegetables, especially leafy greens rich in folic acid, magnesium and carotenes.

- Not eating enough fresh fruit, which is rich in flavonoids that help prevent fluid retention. (Fluid retention is a big cause of raised blood pressure).

- Eating a lot of sugary food which raises your insulin levels too quickly. The extra insulin encourages sticky blood and cholesterol deposits on artery walls.

Don't forget the importance of exercise and (if applicable) giving up smoking.

## INFERTILITY

Before you opt for expensive fertility clinics, why not consider some of the research which shows how faulty nutrition can affect sperm counts and cause miscarriages? No-one has told you about it? That's because nutritional measures come under "self-help". You're assumed to have already done everything to ensure that you are in the best of health.

Some factors known to cause a low sperm count or weak sperm which cannot swim well:

- Selenium, zinc or vitamin C deficiency from eating a faulty diet.

- Excess alcohol and coffee consumption.

- Smoking.

- Environmental oestrogens (toxins in the environment which are very similar to female hormones).

Up to 50 per cent of miscarriages are due to the male partner—sperm defects which prevent the embryo from developing normally, as demonstrated by Swedish research.

Similar nutritional and lifestyle imbalances can affect women's fertility. Women can also be infertile if they are very overweight or underweight.

## IRRITABLE BOWEL SYNDROME

This is a term used by doctors for any combination of

- Bloating and discomfort

- Flatulence

- Pain

- Diarrhoea and/or constipation (alternating)

when no serious disease is present. The treatment consists of helping you to cope with these symptoms.

Causes of IBS include

- Stress

- Food intolerances

- Dysbiosis

If you believe that stress is not the main cause in your case, carry out the Food Intolerance Test on page 156-157 to see if any foods are responsible. If not, you may benefit from the Intestinal Healing Programme on page 160-161.

## MIGRAINE AND HEADACHES

In my experience, the main cause of these is food intolerances, often aggravated by a spinal alignment problem. If your doctor can identify no other cause, a course of chiropractic adjustments, together with carrying out the Food Intolerance Test on page 156-157 and avoiding problem foods, may turn out to be a permanent answer to this distressing problem.

## OSTEOPOROSIS

This is the brittle bone disease which women are prone to develop after the menopause.

Causes include:

- Not getting enough magnesium and other minerals in your diet. Calcium alone is not enough to prevent osteoporosis—research shows that magnesium, zinc and other minerals are needed too.

- Not getting enough exercise.

- Not getting enough vitamin D, found in oily fish and cod liver oil and formed by the action of sunlight on your skin, or enough vitamin K, which is found in fresh vegetables such as broccoli, brussels sprouts, cauliflower and cabbage.

- Osteoporosis is aggravated by eating too much salt, sugar, protein, and phosphorus-containing food additives, especially those in soft drinks.

Beware of hormone replacement therapy. It only protects you while you take it, while at the same time increasing your risk of getting certain cancers. It is also highly addictive. Once you start taking it, it is very difficult to stop because of withdrawal symptoms in the form of severe hot flushes. If you want to come off HRT, do so by very slowly reducing the dose over a period of about one year.

## PROSTATE ENLARGEMENT

This is a problem which can affect men from middle age onwards. It is not difficult to treat by natural means and you should see results within six months. The enlargement of the prostate gland causes problems with urination. It seems to be associated with:

- Not getting enough zinc from food.

- Eating too much saturated fat and not enough essential polyunsaturated oils from nuts and seeds.

Pumpkin seeds are rich in zinc and oils, and have a very good reputation for reducing prostate problems. You may also benefit from taking 15 mg zinc per day in supplemental form, from the herbs Saw Palmetto and horsetail, plus the pollen product Cernilton, which has been used in Sweden for many years.

## WOMEN'S HORMONAL PROBLEMS

(Including period pains in young women, premenstrual syndrome and menopausal hot flushes).

These are mainly due to dietary imbalances and a lack of vitamin– and mineral-rich food, especially B vitamins, zinc and magnesium. Regularly using this recipe book should bring rapid changes in how you feel, although you may also benefit from taking a supplement of magnesium and B vitamins to speed up the process.

One of the best foods to combat menopausal problems is

soya (soy). Follow the recipes in this book, using soya-containing foods as often as you can. Soya is said to be such a good hormone balancer that it is as effective as (and a lot safer than) the drug tamoxifen in preventing breast cancer.

## SKIN PROBLEMS

It should come as no surprise that if you need plenty of vitamin A, zinc, B vitamins, vitamin C and other vitamins and minerals to keep your skin healthy, then if you don't get enough of these you are likely to have a problem skin!

Nutritional deficiencies are a big cause of acne and spotty skin, even in teenagers (it's not a purely hormonal problem). Although spots are often blamed on fatty food, and it is true that fats can clog up your pores, don't forget that fatty foods (like sugary ones) tend to be high in calories and low in vitamins and minerals, and thus cause nutritional deficiencies.

Eczema can also be caused by nutritional deficiencies, but is more often linked to food intolerances, so do carry out the test on page 156-157 if you suffer from it.

Psoriasis is usually caused by nutritional deficiencies and an overloaded liver. Alcohol almost always aggravates psoriasis because it stresses the liver. The Liver Rejuvenation Programme on page 158-159 will probably help you.

Sallow skin is also linked with an overloaded liver, combined with lack of oxygen due to smoking or lack of exercise, and dehydration due to drinking too much tea, coffee and alcohol and too little water.

# Appendix II
# Testing for Food Intolerances

A food intolerance is simply an unpleasant reaction which results from eating a common food. Although often referred to as a food allergy, it does not cause life-threatening reactions, so it is better to keep the two terms separate.

You should carry out this test if you have some of the food intolerance symptoms listed in the questionnaire on page 9. The reason for the test is to find out which foods are responsible, so that you can avoid them if you wish to avoid the symptoms they produce.

I do not recommend any other tests for food intolerances. Blood tests are expensive and unreliable because food does not normally come into contact with your blood. The accuracy of other methods such as kinesiology (muscle testing) and vega testing (electrical measurements carried out on the skin) depends so much on the practitioner's unique gifts that it is a minefield for most of us.

Don't make the mistake of thinking that you can cut corners with this test. For instance, eating a piece of bread and then waiting to see if you get a headache will leave you none the wiser. The four foods which you will test are responsible for over 90 per cent of unidentified food intolerances for one simple reason—we eat them so frequently, often several times every day. If you had an intolerance to

something like avocado pears or tequila you would quickly realize it because you probably don't consume these very often. But an intolerance to a food eaten every day results in symptoms which we take for granted. These symptoms often come and go with no obvious pattern at all. The culprit can only be tracked down by avoiding the main suspects for long enough to allow the symptoms to disappear. They are then reintroduced to see if the symptoms return.

Which foods do most of us eat every day?

**Wheat** (found in bread, flour, biscuits, sauces, puddings etc.)

**Dairy products** (found in milk, cream, cheese, yoghurt, butter, and anything containing these)

**Yeast** (found in alcoholic drinks, stock cubes and other savoury flavourings, gravy mix, bread and pizza)

**Egg** (found in egg dishes, egg pasta, many brands of ice cream, desserts, batter, pancakes etc.)

The instructions for the test are given on the next page. Follow them very carefully, especially the ones which ask you to stick to the recipes in this book. For instance, many convenience foods do not have all their ingredients listed on the label. If you unknowingly eat a little of the test foods when you are not supposed to, the test will not work.

| | Testing Procedure | Results |
|---|---|---|
| **Weeks 1 & 2** | Eat *only* from the recipes and foods in this book. Drink *only* water and the other recommended drinks (see page 17). | |
| **Week 3** | In addition to the nutritional therapy recipes and drinks, also consume egg-free wheat pasta, wheat flour or plain wheat crackers every day for 5 days, then stop. If you get any unpleasant reactions, such as headaches, sinus congestion or severe fatigue, or if your weight rises by several pounds during that time, make a note of them in the Results column and stop eating the wheat before the 5 days is up. There is no point in continuing, because it is extremely likely that you have a wheat intolerance and need to continue avoiding wheat.<br>Whether or not you experience a reaction, stop the wheat after 5 days, and eat nutritional therapy recipes and drinks only for the next two days. | |
| **Week 4** | Repeat what you did in Week 1, consuming cow's milk products daily instead of wheat, particularly fresh milk, cheese and yoghurt. The procedure is exactly the same as for Week 1. | |
| **Week 5** | Repeat what you did in Week 1, consuming eggs daily instead of wheat. If you do not want to eat a whole egg every day, make a 2-egg omelette with plain egg and water, cook it very thinly, and eat a small strip each day for the test period. | |
| **Week 6** | Repeat what you did in Week 1, consuming yeast daily instead of wheat. Buy a small jar of low-sodium yeast extract from a health food shop, and make it into a hot drink with boiling water. Drink this each day for the test period. | |
| **What to do next?** | Any symptoms which did not clear within the first two weeks of this test and return when you tested one of the foods, are probably not due to a food intolerance. Even so, continuing to use the recipes in this book will help you to eat a greater than usual variety of foods. This can help you to avoid developing food intolerances as well as nutritional deficiencies.<br>If you do find that you react badly to one or more foods, you should avoid those foods as best you can for about six months, after which you may find that you can eat them from time to time without a return of your symptoms. You will also probably benefit from the intestinal healing programme on page 160-161, which treats the poor digestion and intestinal inflammation which are thought to be the cause of food intolerances. | |

# Appendix III
# Liver Rejuvenation Programme

This involves (1) Ensuring that your bowels can remove wastes quickly; (2) Helping your gall-bladder to empty out (into your intestine) wastes which it collects from your liver; (3) Helping your liver to make enzymes used to break down toxins.

| Step No. | Procedure | Comments |
|---|---|---|
| 1 | If necessary, ensure regular daily bowel movements, using a varied programme of:<br>• Enemas<br>• Ground linseeds (flax seeds) or psyllium[1]<br>• Epsom salts[1]<br>• Bowel tonic herbs[2] | Daily exercise helps to prevent constipation. Eating dates is also helpful.<br>**Notes**<br>1. One dessert-spoon mixed with a large glass of water.<br>2. As per label instructions. Take no more often than once every three days. |
| 2 | Try to avoid eating any of the foods listed on page 11 or drinking alcohol.Consume the following as often as possible, and use this recipe book as regularly as you can, including the Detoxification Soup on page 39.<br>• Beetroot and beetroot juice<br>• Artichokes<br>• Radishes (including the mooli variety) and radish juice<br>• Watercress<br>• Dandelion coffee<br>• Turmeric (yellow Indian spice)<br>• Broccoli, cabbage, cauliflower, brussels sprouts. Can be made into juices. | Most of these foods help to drain your liver and gall-bladder, ensuring that toxic substances dissolved in your bile reach your intestines as soon as possible, after which a bowel motion will remove them from your body.<br>Broccoli etc. actually help your liver to make detoxifying enzymes.<br>Dandelion coffee can be bought from health food shops. Or make your own by drying and roasting dandelion roots, crushing them and boiling the pieces.<br>If you make your own raw beetroot or radish juice, allow it to stand for 20 minutes before drinking.<br>Avoid drinking grapefruit juice, which can interfere with the action of some of your liver enzymes. |

| Step No. | Procedure | Comments |
|---|---|---|
| 3 | Take the following herbs and supplements daily:<br><br>Magnesium[1] ........................................ 200-500 mg<br>N-acetyl cysteine[2] .............................. 500 mg<br>Reduced glutathione[2] ......................... 500 mg<br>Silymarin[3] ........................................... As per product label<br>Wild Yam[4] .......................................... As per product label<br>Flavonoids[5], especially black grape or cherry skin extracts and pycnogenol.<br>Lecithin[6] ............................................ 1 tablespoon | **Notes**<br>1. Needed for most liver detoxification processes, but assimilation from the blood into the cells is often impaired.<br>2. Strongly liver-protective amino acids.<br>3. Stimulates the gall-bladder, and has a protective and repairing effect on liver cells.<br>4. Helps to prevent pain of liver spasms when liver is overloaded.<br>5. Help to prevent toxins from being formed while the liver is working.<br>6. Helps liver cell membranes to excrete toxins which could damage them.<br>See page 162 for suppliers of these products. |
| 4 | Try to have regular saunas to help your liver by excreting toxins through your skin. | |

Research from Birmingham University in the UK shows that many illnesses are now known
to be caused or aggravated by a liver overload, including parkinsonism, Alzheimer's disease,
motor neurone disease and multiple sclerosis.
This programme should be carried out for at least three months or until no further
improvement is obtained in your health.
If you have any long-term health problems
it is also advisable to repeat it once a year for 4-6 weeks.
See page 162 for sources of any products mentioned in this section.

# Appendix IV
# Intestinal Healing Programme

This three-month Intestinal Healing Programme sets out to reverse the harmful changes shown in the diagram on page 151. This will result in less inflammation in your intestines, due to better digestion and fewer toxin-producing bacteria. You should then suffer less from food intolerances and liver overload problems (see the symptoms listed on page 9).

| Step No. | Procedure | Comments |
|---|---|---|
| 1 | 10 to 20 minutes before eating, slowly drink a small tumbler of water containing a few drops of gentian or golden seal tincture or fluid extract. Ensure that you relax well when eating. Eat slowly and chew your food thoroughly. | The bitter taste of these herbs helps to stimulate stomach acid production. (You must allow yourself to taste the liquid.) Golden seal is also a useful liver herb and an anti-microbial for the intestines. Do not take golden seal in pregnancy. |
| 2 | Half-way through your meal, depending on the size of the meal, take 1-3 capsules of HCl pepsin or betaine hydrochloride. To soothe inflammation in your intestines, drink peppermint, fennel or chamomile tea after meals. | HCl pepsin is a hydrochloric acid supplement. This stomach acid helps to start off the rest of the digestive process. Reduce the dosage if you experience any uncomfortable sensations. Do not take HCl if you have a peptic ulcer. |
| 3 | To reduce harmful bacteria and parasites in your intestines, take grapefruit seed extract for the first two months. If you have ever taken a lot of antibiotics (especially if recently) also take enteric-coated oregano and clove oil capsules. These help to treat candidiasis. Whenever you can, also take one clove of fresh garlic, crushed and mixed with a dessertspoon of olive oil, three times a day. | Follow the directions on the product label when taking these products. See page 162 for where to obtain the products mentioned in this section. |

| Step No. | Procedure | Comments |
|---|---|---|
| 4 | Restrict sweet and starchy food in your diet for the first two months. Try to make your diet 90 per cent as follows:<br>• Fish, chicken and soya products<br>• Vegetables (both cooked and as salads), beans, lentils and chickpeas<br>• Nuts of all types (especially Brazil nuts) and sunflower and sesame seeds.<br>• Olive oil in liberal amounts.<br>During this two months, avoid dried fruit and fruit juices. Make liberal use of cayenne (chilli) pepper, fresh ginger, radishes and cloves. Stir chopped raw garlic into meals before serving. | Starchy food, sugars and grains cannot be digested completely when your intestine is inflamed, because the walls of your intestine cannot produce the necessary enzymes. By avoiding these foods for two months you reduce the amount of undigested food particles that feed toxin-producing bacteria and yeasts.<br>Garlic and the spices mentioned help to control these undesirable micro-organisms. |
| 5 | After the first two months, your intestines should be getting less inflamed. It is now time to begin replacing your beneficial intestinal bacteria. Take a guaranteed quality combination of Acidophilus/Bifudus bacteria for one month. | Not all products contain live beneficial bacteria. Those in yoghurt are killed by stomach juices. To repopulate your intestine an acid-resistant product is required. For the first seven days, "Replete", although expensive, is ideal. See page 162 for suppliers. |
| 6 | It is also time to start using tissue-restorative herbs:<br>Comfrey tea: 1 cup (double-strength) with each meal. Once a day combine this with slippery elm. Also drink the juice of fresh cabbage leaves as often as you can with meals.<br>Biocare's Enteroplex: 1 capsule with each meal. Contains a combination of herbal liquorice and cabbage extract. | Always rinse your washing-up. Traces of detergent can damage delicate intestinal cell membranes.<br>Cabbage juice is an excellent gut healer. You can omit the Enteroplex provided you drink this juice with every meal. Comfrey is a great healer which has sometimes had a bad press, but only when used in massive amounts. |
| 7 | If your gut symptoms have not improved after this three-month programme, you are advised to obtain a special stool analysis (CDSA). This can be arranged through a nutritional therapist. Be patient; successful treatment can take time. | The test will show which types of irritant bacteria are still damaging your intestines, and the best anti-microbials to use against them. |

# WHERE TO FIND THE PRODUCTS AND SERVICES MENTIONED

UK sources. See Useful Addresses on next page for contact details
and for US or international suppliers of equivalent products,

## This list does not include foods, which are covered on pages 22 to 26

Acidophilus/bifidus[1]

Bowel tonic herbs[2]

Comfrey tea[5]

Dandelion coffee[5]

Enteric-coated oregano
and clove oil[6]

Enteroplex[1]

Epsom salts (magnesium
sulphate)[7]

Flavonoid supplements[10]

Food supplements[9]

Gentian fluid extract[2]

Golden seal fluid extract[2]

Grapefruit seed extract[1]

HCl pepsin[10]

Herbal teas[5]

Juice extractors[11]

Laxatives[3]

Lecithin[5]

Linseeds (flax seeds)[5]

Magnesium supplements[9]

N-acetyl cysteine (NAC)[10]

Nutritional therapists[12]

Psyllium[3]

Pumpkin seeds[5]

Reduced glutathione[1]

Replete[1]

Silymarin[2]

Slippery elm[2]

**NOTES**

1. Recommended brand is Biocare.
2. Recommended brand is Herbs of Grace.
3. Herbs of Grace Tri-Cleanse brand recommended.
4. "BTA" by Herbs of Grace is recommended.
5. From health shops.
6. Combined in Candicidin by Biocare.
7. Available from pharmacies.
8. Procydin by Biocare recommended. Solgar products are also good.
9. Good quality multivitamin and multimineral brands include Quest, Solgar, Biocare, Cantassium and Lamberts.
10. Brands available by Biocare, Solgar and Lamberts.
11. From many high street electrical shops.
12. See *British Association of Nutritional Therapists* and *American Naturopathic Medical Association* under Useful Addresses.

# USEFUL ADDRESSES

- **Allergy Research Group**, 30806 Santana St, Hayward, CA 94544, USA. Tel: +1 800 408 4274. U.S. suppliers of quality food supplements.
- **American Naturopathic Medical Association**, P.O.Box 96273 Las Vegas, Nev 89193, USA. Tel: 702 897 7053. Contact them for practitioners who can help you with your health problems.
- **Ardovries Shearway Ltd**, Smarden Road, Headcorn, Kent TN27 9TA, UK. Tel: 01622 891199. Suppliers of frozen blueberries, Black Forest Fruits etc. to supermarkets, cash & carries and freezer centres. Phone to find stockists.
- **Biocare Ltd**, Lakeside, 180 Lifford Lane, King's Norton, Birmingham B30 3NU, UK. Tel: +44 (0)121 433 3727. Suppliers of dietary supplements, and potassium salt and baking powder.
- **British Association of Nutritional Therapists** BCM BANT, London WC1N 3XX, UK. Send £2 for a register of practitioners in the UK who can help you with your health problems.
- **Clearspring Ltd**, Unit 19a Acton Park Estate, London W3 7QE, UK. Tel: 020 8746 0152. International mail order and wholesale suppliers of macrobiotic and Japanese foods, including miso, wasabi sauce, tamari sauce, agar and umeboshi plum sauce.
- **http://www.healthshop.com** International Internet suppliers of food supplements at discount prices.
- **Herbs of Grace**, 5a Lanwades Business Park, Kennett, Newmarket, Suffolk CB8 7PN, UK. Tel: +44 (0)1638 750140.
- **Infinity Foods Co-operative Ltd**, 67 Norway St, Portslade, Brighton BN41 1AE, UK. Tel: 01273 424060. Wholesale suppliers of many wholefoods including chestnut flour, dried chestnuts, and sweet (glutinous) brown rice. Phone to find stockists.
- **KTC (Edibles) Ltd**, J.S. House, Moorcroft Drive, Wednesbury, WS10 7DE, UK. Tel: 0121 505 9200. Suppliers of coconut oil. Phone to find stockists.
- **The Nutri Centre**, 7 Park Crescent, London W1N 3HE, UK. Tel: 020 7436 5122. Shop and mail order supplier of all available dietary and herbal supplements in the UK.
- **Source Foods**, 9 Cwm Business Centre, Marine St, Cwm, Ebbw Vale, Gwent NP3 6TB, UK. Tel: 01495 371 698. Suppliers of high quality organic miso. Several different varieties, including pale. Phone to find stockists or for mail order.
- **Summerfrost Ltd**, Arctic House, Rye Lane, Dunton Green, Sevenoaks, Kent TN14 5HB, UK. Tel: 01732 459455. Suppliers of frozen blueberries and other fruits to Harrods and other stores in the South East. Phone to find stockists.
- **Thorne Research Inc**, PO Box 3200, Sandpoint, Idaho 83864, USA. Tel: +1 800 228 1966. U.S. suppliers of quality food supplements.
- **Windmill Organics**, 161 Dawes Road, London SW6 7EE, UK. Tel: 020 7924 2300. Suppliers of chestnut flour and other products to the UK market. Phone to find stockists.

# RECIPE INDEX

# GENERAL INDEX